Visual Perception: The Nineteenth Century

PERSPECTIVES IN PSYCHOLOGY

William Kessen
George Mandler
General Editors

George A. Miller
Mathematics and Psychology

Jean Matter Mandler and George Mandler
Thinking: From Association to Gestalt

William N. Dember
Visual Perception: The Nineteenth Century

Visual Perception:
The Nineteenth
Century

William N. Dember

University of Cincinnati

New York · London · Sydney John Wiley & Sons, Inc.

Library of Congress Catalog Card Number: 64-25895
Printed in the United States of America

This little book is dedicated to my little girls,
Joanna and Laura

Foreword

Perspectives in Psychology is a series of original books written for psychologists and students who are concerned with the history of ideas in psychology.

It is our intention to present fresh and thoughtful assessments of the current psychological scene in the context of relevant historical changes. Many authors of the *Perspectives* books will examine a selected slice of the history of psychology by way of selected and annotated readings. This is not to say that *Perspectives* is a uniform or systematic encyclopedia of the history of psychology. Psychologists, by disposition and training, are reluctant to work their ideas into a standard weave—homespun or exotic—and *Perspectives* represents well the happy diversity of the discipline.

Some books in the series are scholarly disquisitions on the historical antecedents of a current problem in psychological analysis; some books move—after a brief glance at historical antecedents—directly toward a discussion of contemporary psychology and its future; some books deal with the past largely as a platform for polemical exposition. And, occasionally, *Perspectives* will present an original work in psychology that escapes the historical definition altogether.

Perspectives in Psychology, by using the avenues of documented history and informed discussions of current as well as classical issues, will emphasize that psychology has a history as well as a past and that it advances as it grows.

WILLIAM KESSEN
GEORGE MANDLER

Preface

The aim of this book is to make readily available to students of perception and to students of the history of psychology a sample of the theoretical and empirical writings on visual perception published in the nineteenth century. A companion book, covering material from the present century, is in preparation. Hopefully the two together will offer the reader a picture of the development of this diffuse and variegated area of investigation that might enable him better to appreciate contemporary research and theory.

In selecting passages for the present volume, I was aided, but also somewhat constrained, by the models provided by the two major texts offering readings in the history of psychology, Rand's and Dennis's. Some overlap with these books was unavoidable; there *are* classics in the psychological literature, and since nineteenth-century psychology was so heavily committed to the topic of perception, many of these classics are appropriate for inclusion in a volume restricted to that topic. Along with Rand and Dennis, similar help in selection and interpretation has come from E. G. Boring, in the form of his two famous works, *A History of Experimental Psychology* and *Sensation and Perception in the History of Experimental Psychology*.

I would also like to acknowledge the very material assistance in the preparation of this book provided by Mr. Alfred Bricka, who made reproductions of many of the passages, and not always under optimal circumstances; by Dr. John Swets, who read the manuscript and greatly encouraged me with his kind comments; and by Professors Kessen and Mandler, whose central role in the

production of this book was even greater than may be evident
from their function as editors of the series of which it is a part.

W. N. DEMBER

Cincinnati, Ohio
July, 1964

Contents

Introduction

All of science is based ultimately in man's sensory experience. The various classical "natural sciences," for example, physics, chemistry, geology, and astronomy, differ from each other primarily in the aspects of experience on which they focus. This difference, of course, leads to further differences among the scientific disciplines, as, for example, in methodology, instrumentation, type and level of theory construction, extent of reliance on mathematics, and so on.

Experience lies at the base of all these fields in two direct and obvious ways. First, it suggests the problems that arouse man's curiosity, which in turn motivates speculation and perhaps eventually culminates in the development of a formal structure of abstract concepts and relations that we recognize as a scientific theory. Thus, modern astronomy, in all its technical and theoretical splendor, may have had its genesis in the experience of a lonely shepherd gazing in awe at "the night sky scattered thick with stars."

No scientific theory, however elegant and however apparently "true," can stand for long without being tested. This almost compulsive continual self-criticism and striving for perfection is perhaps the major differentiating feature of science as compared with other approaches to knowledge and truth, for example, religion or art. And here is where experience enters again most obviously in the scientific enterprise, for theories are tested against the facts of experience.

In the early stages of a science, the experience referred to is usually unrefined and unaided by artificial devices, but as the field develops, elaborate technical equipment often intervenes between the scientist and the objects of his observation. The shepherd used his "naked eye"; the modern astronomer uses high-powered telescopes, spectroscopes, and electronic computers. Indeed, the various sciences are frequently identified by the layman in terms of their characteristic types of apparatus (astronomy, the telescope; chemistry, the test tube; bacteriology, the microscope; sub-atomic physics, the bubble chamber).

The point of many of these devices is not only to increase the sensitivity and precision of man's experience, but also to minimize the role of the fallible and biased human observer in the process of data collection. Thus, it happens that in the well-developed fields, such as physics, the type of experience that is invoked in theory testing is only very indirectly related to the events being studied, perhaps taking the form of reading the printed output of an electronic computer.

It also happens in the well-developed scientific disciplines that the first function of experience is similarly minimized. Problems for investigation are less and less frequently suggested by the scientist's sensory encounters with the interesting events of the "physical world" and more and more by his intellectual encounters with highly abstract formalized sets of concepts and relations and their logical implications.

Nevertheless, despite the relatively impersonal character of much of present-day science, its origin and base still lie in human experience. The acceptance of this proposition—that knowledge, or at least scientific knowledge, is grounded in experience—has led to considerable speculation about the manner in which sensory experience can convey information about the nature of the "physical world." Such speculation became the province of a branch of philosophy called *epistemology*. Epistemological speculation, of course, is not confined to professional philosophers; every scientist must do a bit of it himself, privately and sometimes publicly, to reassure himself and his colleagues that their endeavors as scientists do have meaning and that the approach being used is a valid one for its intended purpose.

Note that in the realm of epistemology, experience, which for the natural sciences is but a starting point and even only a tool or instrument, becomes the *object* of investigation. Note further that when the methods and strategies of the scientific approach are brought to bear on the problem of experience—when the instrument of experience is focused on itself—then a new science is created, the science of experience. Such a science, like the others, has its roots deep in history, but as a self-conscious discipline, named, organized, institutionalized, and with its own characteristic apparatus, techniques, theories, heroes, and so on, its beginnings can best be found in the nineteenth century, and its name is Psychology.

Contemporary psychology is, of course, a field of great diversity, and it has diverse origins including, along with epistemology, physiology (especially the physiology of the "special senses"), physics, biology, medicine, education, anthropology, and a host of other disciplines, scientific and otherwise. Even so, in its beginnings psychology was the "science of experience." Then, for some time after the Behavioristic revolt, led by John Watson in the second and third decades of the present century, experience, as suitable subject matter for scientific investigation, was suppressed and psychology became the "science of behavior." At the present time, compromise definitions of psychology are often given, enabling the re-entry of experience into the field either openly or under a behavioristic guise.

In modern textbooks and professional journals the experiential area of the broad field of psychology is usually identified by the labels "sensation" and "perception." Whether both labels are necessary, that is, whether it is meaningful to distinguish between the two, whether the two are adequate to cover the area, indeed just what "sensation" and "perception" mean, these are questions that need not be answered here, for these and many others are the stuff of which this volume is made. For the sake of convenience, however, the single term *perception* will be employed to refer to this broad area, within which some theorists prefer to make much finer distinctions.

The purpose of this volume is to present a sample of what was thought and done about perception in the nineteenth century. The sample is hardly unbiased, however. The passages included were selected on the basis of several criteria. One obvious criterion was that the passages should be representative of the concerns and interests, both theoretical and empirical, of those working in the area of perception in the nineteenth century. Another was to include, where possible, "firsts" in a field, as for example the first report in the scientific literature of reversible figures (see the comment by Necker in Chapter 3). A third criterion was to seek material that was to have a "future"—material that gives meaning to, and derives meaning from, present-day ideas. A fourth basis of selection was the readability and intrinsic interest of the passages, aside from any historical significance they might have.

In addition to the above criteria for inclusion, there was one explicit exclusion criterion. Because this volume is to be one of a set, which will contain a separate volume on *psychophysics*, passages directly concerned with that topic (and the literature of the nineteenth century is replete with them) were intentionally not included. Therefore the writings of neither Weber nor Fechner, for example, are sampled in the present volume.

Finally, and with considerable regret, it was decided not to include passages from the works of the philosopher-psychologists who might be labeled "pre-Gestaltists," such as Brentano, von Ehrenfels, and Meinong; those parts of their writing most directly relevant to the topic of perception were not available in English translation. Their point of view will be represented, however, in the passages from the Gestalt theorists that will appear in a companion volume to the present one covering perception in the twentieth century.

To assure comprehensiveness of coverage, it was necessary that each of the reprinted passages be relatively brief. In some instances it was possible to reproduce an article in its entirety; in most, however, considerable abridgment was essential. The reader is urged, then, to think of this volume more as a menu than a meal, and to go to the original sources when his appetite so dictates.

Anatomical and Neural Substrates

Much of contemporary work in the area of perception (as well as other areas of psychology) is the exploring of the physical and physiological bases of the psychological phenomena. This exploration includes attempts *(a)* to specify the "adequate stimuli" for each of the sense modalities and the precise physical correlates of the sensory attributes within a modality (for example, the identification of wave frequency as the primary physical correlate of the auditory attribute of pitch); *(b)* to describe the mechanics (including anatomical structure and biochemistry) of the sense organs and the ways in which they transform the physical energy of the stimulus into neural impulses; *(c)* to discover the nature of these neural impulses, the pathways they follow, their temporal patterning, their interactions with other ongoing neural activities, and their ultimate fate in the higher neural centers; *(d)* and, the biggest mystery of them all, to understand how this neural activity is "decoded" into perceptual experience, from one point of view, or, from a more nearly neutral point of view, into information about the nature of the stimulus objects which originally gave rise to the neural activity.

The state of knowledge of these different aspects of the problem varies from one sense modality to another and varies considerably from one aspect of the problem to another. One general rule seems to be that the extent and certainty of knowledge vary inversely with the anatomical depth to which the scientist probes the sensory systems.

The four passages in this chapter are classics in the history of man's investigation of the physico-physiological bases of his experience. The first is taken from a much longer article by Thomas Young in which he presents a mass of evidence, both clinical and experimental, that convincingly assigns to the lens of the eye the function of accommodation, the process whereby objects at varying distances from the observer are brought into, and maintained in, focus. This is a proposition so well documented that it now enjoys the status of a "fact"; it is, indeed, by now so well known that it is easy to forget the difficulty and ingenuity with which it was originally demonstrated.

Young's article in its entirety requires careful study for a full understanding of the details of his argument. The excerpts reproduced here can do little more than suggest the salient points of his complex and elaborate presentation.

Thomas Young

On the Mechanism of the Eye

In the year 1793, I had the honour of laying before the Royal Society, some observations on the faculty by which the eye accommodates itself to the perception of objects at different distances. The opinion which I then entertained, although it had never been placed exactly in the same light, was neither so new, nor so much forgotten, as was supposed by myself, and by most of those with whom I had any intercourse on the subject. Mr.

T. Young. The Bakerian lecture, On the mechanism of the eye. *Philosophical Transactions*, Royal Society of London, 1801, [91]. 23–88 plus plates.

Hunter, who had long before formed a similar opinion, was still less aware of having been anticipated in it, and was engaged, at the time of his death, in an investigation of the facts relative to it; an investigation for which, as far as physiology was concerned, he was undoubtedly well qualified. Mr. Home, with the assistance of Mr. Ramsden, whose recent loss this Society cannot but lament, continued the inquiry which Mr. Hunter had begun; and the results of his experiments appeared very satisfactorily to confute the hypothesis of the muscularity of the crystalline lens. I therefore thought it incumbent on me, to take the earliest opportunity of testifying my persuasion of the justice of Mr. Home's conclusions, which I accordingly mentioned in a Dissertation published at Gottingen in 1796, and also in an Essay presented last year to this Society. About three months ago, I was induced to resume the subject, by perusing Dr. Porterfield's paper on the internal motions of the eye; and I have very unexpectedly made some observations, which I think I may venture to say, appear to be finally conclusive in favour of my former opinion, as far as that opinion attributed to the lens a power of changing its figure. At the same time, I must remark, that every person who has been engaged in experiments of this nature, will be aware of the extreme delicacy and precaution requisite, both in conducting them, and in drawing inferences from them; and will also readily allow, that no apology is necessary for the fallacies which have misled many others, as well as myself, in the application of those experiments to optical and physiological determinations.

Besides the inquiry respecting the accommodation of the eye to different distances, I shall have occasion to notice some other particulars relative to its functions; and I shall begin with a general consideration of the sense of vision. I shall then enumerate some dioptrical propositions subservient to my purposes, and describe an instrument for readily ascertaining the focal distance of the eye. On these foundations, I shall investigate the dimensions and refractive powers of the human eye in its quiescent state; and the form and magnitude of the picture which is delineated on the retina. I shall next inquire, how great are the changes which the eye admits, and what degree of alteration in its proportions will be necessary for these changes, on the various suppositions

that are principally deserving of comparison. I shall proceed to
relate a variety of experiments which appear to be the most
proper to decide on the truth of each of these suppositions, and
to examine such arguments as have been brought forwards,
against the opinion which I shall endeavour to maintain; and I
shall conclude with some anatomical illustrations of the capacity
of the organs of various classes of animals, for the functions attributed to them. . . .

* * *

Following the introductory remarks quoted above, and some
that have been omitted, Young presents three types of material:
first are what he calls his "dioptrical propositions," in which the
optical properties of the eye are given in precise mathematical
detail; second, an instrument is described, an "optometer," by
which the refractive power of the eye can be measured; third,
through use of the optometer, and interpretation of the measurements so taken according to the model provided by the dioptrical
propositions, Young provides specific refractive values for his own
eye.

In the passage that immediately follows, Young then goes on to
inquire into the possible mechanisms whereby the range in refractive power exhibited by his own eye might be effected. Four
hypothetical accommodative mechanisms are suggested: (1) a
change in the curvature of the cornea; (2) a change in the distance from lens to retina; (3) a combination of 1 and 2 above: (4)
a change in the shape of the lens. The implications of these hypotheses are spelled out below, and in sufficiently fine mathematical detail to allow for discriminating empirical test.

* * *

. . . I shall take the range of my own eye, as being probably
about the medium, and inquire what changes will be necessary in

order to produce it; whether we suppose the radius of the cornea to be diminished, or the distance of the lens from the retina to be increased, or these two causes to act conjointly, or the figure of the lens itself to undergo an alteration.

1. We have calculated, that when the eye is in a state of relaxation, the refraction of the cornea is such as to collect rays diverging from a point ten inches distant, to a focus at the distance of 13⅔ tenths. In order that it may bring to the same focus, rays diverging from a point distant 29 tenths, we find ... that its radius must be diminished from 31 to 25 hundredths, or very nearly in the ratio of five to four.

2. Supposing the change from perfect vision at ten inches to 29 tenths, to be effected by a removal of the retina to a greater distance from the lens, this will require ... an elongation of 135 thousandths, or more than one-seventh of the diameter of the eye. . . .

3. If the radius of the cornea be diminished one-sixteenth, or to 29 hundredths, the eye must at the same time be elongated 97 thousandths, or about one-ninth of its diameter.

4. Supposing the crystalline lens to change its form; if it became a sphere, its diameter would be 28 hundredths, and, its anterior surface retaining its situation, the eye would have perfect vision at the distance of an inch and a half. . . . This is more than double the actual change. But it is impossible to determine precisely how great an alteration of form is necessary, without ascertaining the nature of the curves into which its surface may be changed. If it were always a spheroid more or less oblate, the focal length of each surface would vary inversely as the square of the axis: but, if the surfaces became, from spherical, portions of hyperbolic conoids, or of oblong spheroids, or changed from more obtuse to more acute figures of this kind, the focal length would vary more rapidly. Disregarding the elongation of the axis, and supposing the curvature of each surface to be changed proportionally, the radius of the anterior must become about 24, and that of the posterior 17 hundredths. . . .

*   *   *

Having presented and elaborated on the possible accommodatory mechanisms, Young takes up each one in turn and considers the evidence pertinent to it. First, he examines the corneal curvature-change hypothesis and reports several experiments, all of which indirectly cast serious doubt on its tenability. In the passage below, a much more direct experimental attack is described. It is shown that normal accommodation is still evident with elimination of the refractive power of the cornea, and therefore with *changes* in its refractive power also entirely eliminated.

*   *   *

. . . But a much more accurate and decisive experiment remains. I take out of a small botanical microscope, a double convex lens, of eight-tenths radius and focal distance, fixed in a socket one-fifth of an inch in depth; securing its edges with wax, I drop into it a little water, nearly cold, till it is three-fourths full, and then apply it to my eye, so that the cornea enters half-way into the socket, and is everywhere in contact with the water. . . . My eye immediately becomes presbyopic, and the refractive power of the lens, which is reduced by the water to a foçal length of about 16 tenths . . . is not sufficient to supply the place of the cornea, rendered inefficacious by the intervention of the water; but the addition of another lens, of five inches and a half focus, restores my eye to its natural state, and somewhat more. I then apply the optometer, and I find the same inequality in the horizontal and vertical refractions as without the water; and I have, in both directions, a power of accommodation equivalent to a focal length of four inches, as before. At first sight indeed, the accommodation appears to be somewhat less, and only able to bring the eye from the state fitted for parallel rays to a focus at five inches distance; and this made me once imagine, that the cornea might have some slight effect in the natural state; but, considering that the artificial cornea was about a tenth of an inch before the place of the natural cornea, I calculated the effect of this difference, and found it exactly sufficient to account for the diminution of the range of vision. I cannot ascertain the distance of the glass lens from the cornea to the hundredth of an inch; but the error cannot be much greater, and it may be on either side.

After this, it is almost necessary to apologize for having stated the former experiments; but, in so delicate a subject, we cannot have too great a variety of concurring evidence.

* * *

Having discounted the hypothesis that accommodation is effected through change in corneal curvature, Young then describes a series of experiments, and related anatomical evidence, that disconfirm the second of the four hypothetical mechanisms. The third hypothesis, a combination of 1 and 2, is then glossed over as highly unlikely, and rightly so. The remainder of the paper is devoted to the fourth, and preferred, hypothesis that identifies change in the shape of the lens as the mechanism of accommodation.

Note especially, in what follows, how Young relies on data from a variety of sources to make his case. He examines people who have had their lenses removed, taking advantage of "nature's experiments." He does experiments and takes measurements on the normal lens. He considers evidence offered by comparative anatomical study of the lens. He looks at the lens under the microscope. Finally, he attends to the mechanism behind the mechanism —the ciliary muscles that presumably control the shape of the lens, and *their* histology and comparative anatomy—and shows how what must happen can happen.

This work of Young's is truly a masterpiece of scientific investigation. And, recall, it was reported in the year when Thomas Jefferson was inaugurated as President of the United States and Beethoven composed his First Symphony.

* * *

. . . It now remains to inquire into the pretensions of the crystalline lens to the power of altering the focal length of the eye.

The grand objection to the efficacy of a change of figure in the lens, was derived from the experiments in which those who have been deprived of it have appeared to possess the faculty of accommodation.

My friend Mr. Ware, convinced as he was of the neatness and accuracy of the experiments related in the Croonian Lecture for 1795, yet could not still help imagining, from the obvious advantage all his patients found, after the extraction of the lens, in using two kinds of spectacles, that there must, in such cases, be a deficiency in the faculty. This circumstance, combined with a consideration of the directions very judiciously given by Dr. Porterfield, for ascertaining the point in question, first made me wish to repeat the experiments upon various individuals, and with the instrument which I have above described as an improvement of Dr. Porterfield's optometer: and I must here acknowledge my great obligation to Mr. Ware, for the readiness and liberality with which he introduced me to such of his numerous patients as he thought most likely to furnish a satisfactory determination. It is unnecessary to enumerate every particular experiment; but the universal result is, contrary to the expectation with which I entered on the inquiry, that in an eye deprived of the crystalline lens, the actual focal distance is totally unchangeable. This will appear from a selection of the most decisive observations.

1. Mr. R. can read at four inches and at six only, with the same glass. He saw the double lines meeting at three inches, and always at the same point; but the cornea was somewhat irregularly prominent, and his vision not very distinct; nor had I, at the time I saw him, a convenient apparatus.

I afterwards provided a small optometer, with a lens of less than two inches focus, adding a series of letters, not in alphabetical order, and projected into such a form as to be most legible at a small inclination. The excess of the magnifying power had the advantage of making the lines more divergent, and their crossing more conspicuous; and the letters served for more readily naming the distance of the intersection, and, at the same time, for judging of the extent of the power of distinguishing objects too near or too remote for perfect vision. . . .

2. Mr. J. had not an eye very proper for the experiment; but he appeared to distinguish the letters at 2½ inches, and at less than an inch. This at first persuaded me, that he must have a power of changing the focal distance: but I afterwards recollected that he had withdrawn his eye considerably, to look at the nearer letters, and had partly closed his eyelids, no doubt contracting at the same time the aperture of the pupil; an action which, even in a perfect eye, always accompanies the change of focus. . . .

3. Miss H., a young lady of about twenty, had a very narrow pupil, and I had not an opportunity of trying the small optometer: but, when she once saw an object double through the slits, no exertion could make it appear single at the same distance. She used for distant objects a glass of 4½ inches focus; with this she could read as far off as 12 inches, and as near as five: for nearer objects she added another of equal focus, and could then read at 7 inches, and at 2½.

4. Hanson, a carpenter, aged 63, had a cataract extracted a few years since from one eye; the pupil was clear and large, and he saw well to work with a lens of 2⅜ inches focus; and could read at 8 and at 15 inches, but most conveniently at 11. With the same glass, the lines of the optometer appeared always to meet at 11 inches; but he could not perceive that they crossed, the line being too strong, and the intersection too distant. The experiment was afterwards repeated with the small optometer: he read the letters from 2 to 3 inches; but the intersection was always at 2½ inches. He now fully understood the circumstances that were to be noticed, and saw the crossing with perfect distinctness: at one time, he said it was a tenth of an inch nearer; but I observed that he had removed his eye two or three tenths from the glass, a circumstance which accounted for this small difference.

5. Notwithstanding Hanson's age, I consider him as a very fair subject for the experiment. But a still more unexceptionable eye was that of Mrs. Maberly. She is about 30, and had the crystalline of both eyes extracted a few years since, but sees best with her right. She walks without glasses; and, with the assistance of a lens of about four inches focus, can read and work with ease. She could distinguish the letters of the small optometer from an inch

to 2½ inches; but the intersection was invariably at the same point, about 19 tenths of an inch distant. A portion of the capsule is stretched across the pupil, and causes her to see remote objects double, when without her glasses; nor can she, by any exertion, bring the two images nearer together, although the exertion makes them more distinct, no doubt by contracting the pupil. The experiment with the optometer was conducted, in the presence of Mr. Ware, with patience and perseverance; nor was any opinion given to make her report partial. . . .

From . . . investigation of the change of the figure of the lens, it appears that the action which I formerly attributed to the external coats, cannot afford an explanation of the phenomenon. The necessary effect of such an action would be, to produce a figure approaching to that of an oblate spheroid; and, to say nothing of the inconvenience attending a diminution of the diameter of the lens, the lateral refraction would be much more increased than the central; nor would the slight change of density, at an equal distance from the axis, be at all equivalent to the increase of curvature: we must therefore suppose some different mode of action in the power producing the change. Now, whether we call the lens a muscle or not, it seems demonstrable, that such a change of figure takes place as can be produced by no external cause; and we may at least illustrate it by a comparison with the usual action of muscular fibres. A muscle never contracts, without at the same time swelling laterally, and it is of no consequence which of the effects we consider as primary. I was induced, by an occasional opacity, to give the name of membranous tendons to the radiations from the centre of the lens; but, on a more accurate examination, nothing really analogous to tendon can be discovered. And, if it were supposed that the parts next the axis were throughout of a tendinous, and therefore unchangeable nature, the contraction must be principally effected by the lateral parts of the fibres; so that the coats would become thicker towards the margin, by their contraction, while the general alteration of form would require them to be thinner; and there would be a contrariety in the actions of the various parts. But, if we compare the central parts of each surface to the belly of the muscle, there is no difficulty in conceiving their thickness to be immediately increased, and to produce an immediate elongation of the axis, and an increase of the central curvature; while the lateral parts co-operate more or less, according to their distance from the centre, and in different individuals in somewhat different proportions. On this supposition, we have no longer any difficulty in attributing a power of change to the crystalline of fishes. M. Petit, in a great number of observations, uniformly found the lens of fishes more or less flattened: but, even if it were not, a slight extension of the lateral part of the superficial fibres would allow those softer coats to become thicker at each vertex, and to form the whole lens into a spheroid somewhat oblong; and here, the lens being the only agent in refraction, a less alteration than in other animals would be sufficient. It is also worthy of inquiry, whether the state of contraction may not immediately add to the refractive power. According to the old experiment, by which Dr. Goddard attempted to show that muscles become more dense as they contract, such an effect might naturally be expected. That experiment is, however, very indecisive, and the opinion is indeed generally exploded, but perhaps too hastily; and whoever shall ascertain the existence or non-existence of such a condensation, will render essential service to physiology in general. . . .

Considering the sympathy of the crystalline lens with the uvea, and the delicate nature of the change of its figure, there is little reason to expect that any artificial stimulus would be more successful in exciting a contractive action in the lens, than it has hitherto been in the uvea; much less would that contraction be visible without art. Soon after Mr. Hunter's death, I pursued the experiment which he had suggested, for ascertaining how far such a contraction might be observable. My apparatus . . . was executed by Mr. Jones. It consisted of a wooden vessel blacked within, which was to be filled with cool, and then with warmer water: a plane speculum was placed under it; a perforation in the bottom was filled with a plate of glass; proper rings were fixed for the reception of the lens, or of the whole eye, and also wires for transmitting electricity: above these, a piece of ground and painted glass, for receiving the image, was supported by a bracket, which moved by a pivot, in connection with a scale divided into fiftieths of an inch. With this apparatus I made some experiments, assisted by Mr. Wilkinson, whose residence was near a slaughter-house: but we could obtain, by this method, no satisfactory evidence of the change; nor was our expectation much disappointed. I understand also, that another member of this Society was equally unsuccessful, in attempting to produce a conspicuous change in the lens by electricity.

In man and in the most common quadrupeds, the structure of the lens is nearly similar. The number of radiations is of little consequence; but I find that in the human crystalline there are ten on each side . . . not three, as I once, from a hasty observation, concluded. Those who find any difficulty in discovering the fibres, must have a sight very ill adapted to microscopical researches. I have laboured with the most obstinate perseverance to trace nerves into the lens, and I have sometimes imagined that I had succeeded; but I cannot positively go further than to state my full conviction of their existence, and of the precipitancy of those who have absolutely denied it. . . .

I consider myself as being partly repaid for the labour lost in search of the nerves of the lens, by having acquired a more accurate conception of the nature and situation of the ciliary substance. It had already been observed, that in the hare and in the wolf, the ciliary processes are not attached to the capsule of the lens; and if by the ciliary processes we understand those filaments which are seen detached after tearing away the capsule, and consist of ramifying vessels, the observation is equally true of the common quadrupeds, and I will venture to say, of the human eye. . . .

. . . I shall now finally recapitulate the principal objects and results of the investigation which I have taken the liberty of detailing so fully to the Royal Society. First, the determination of the refractive power of a variable medium, and its application to the constitution of the crystalline lens. Secondly, the construction of an instrument for ascertaining, upon inspection, the exact focal distance of every eye, and the remedy for its imperfections. Thirdly, to show the accurate adjustment of every part of the eye, for seeing with distinctness the greatest possible extent of objects at the same instant. Fourthly, to measure the collective dispersion of coloured rays in the eye. Fifthly, by immerging the eye in water, to demonstrate that its accommodation does not depend on any change in the curvature of the cornea. Sixthly, by confining the eye at the extremities of its axis, to prove that no material alteration of its length can take place. Seventhly, to examine what inference can be drawn from the experiments hitherto made on persons deprived of the lens; to pursue the inquiry, on the principles suggested by Dr. Porterfield; and to confirm his opinion of the utter inability of such persons to change the refractive state of the organ. Eighthly, to deduce, from the aberration of the lateral rays, a decisive argument in favour of a change in the figure of the crystalline; to ascertain, from the quantity of this aberration, the form into which the lens appears to be thrown in my own eye, and the mode by which the change must be produced in that of every other person. And I flatter myself, that I shall not be deemed too precipitate, in denominating this series of experiments satisfactorily demonstrative.

*   *   *

Whereas Young's research explores the accommodative mechanism of the eye and does so necessarily at a relatively peripheral level (the level of the receptor organ), Charles Bell, in his investigations, takes us deeper into the nervous system. In the next passage Bell describes the research that first demonstrated that the spinal nerves, which contain both afferent (sensory) and efferent (motor) fibers, have their origin in the spinal cord in separate sensory and motor roots. Bell found that the sensory fibers enter the spinal cord via the dorsal roots, while motor fibers emerge from the ventral roots. This same observation was made independently, and perhaps more convincingly, by Magendie in France at about the same time as Bell's; it eventually assumed the status of a law, known as the Bell-Magendie Law after its co-discoverers.

Charles Bell

Idea of a New Anatomy of the Brain

The want of any consistent history of the Brain and Nerves, and the dull unmeaning manner which is in use of demonstrating the brain, may authorize any novelty in the manner of treating the subject.

I have found some of my friends so mistaken in their conception of the object of the demonstrations which I have delivered in my lectures, that I wish to vindicate myself at all hazards. They would have it that I am in search of the seat of the soul; but I wish only to investigate the structure of the brain, as we examine the structure of the eye and ear.

It is not more presumptuous to follow the tracts of nervous matter in the brain, and to attempt to discover the course of sensation, than it is to trace the rays of light through the humours of the eye, and to say, that the retina is the seat of vision. Why are we to close the investigation with the discovéry of the external organ?

It would have been easy to have given this Essay an imposing splendour, by illustrations and engravings of the parts, but I submit it as a sketch to those who are well able to judge of it in this shape.

The prevailing doctrine of the anatomical schools, is that the whole brain is a common sensorium; that the extremities of the nerves are organized, so that each is fitted to receive a peculiar

C. Bell. Idea of a new anatomy of the brain. Privately printed, 1811. This selection is drawn from [Alexander Shaw] reprint of the "Idea of a new anatomy of the brain; submitted for the obervations of his friends; by Charles Bell, F.R.S.E." To which are added selections from letters written by the author of the essay to his brother, Professor George Joseph Bell, between the years 1807 and 1821. *J. anat. Physiol.*, 1869 [November, 1868], **3**, 147–182. This selection—Bell's *Idea* proper—appears in pp. 153–166.

impression; or that they are distinguished from each other only by delicacy of structure, and by a corresponding delicacy of sensation, that the nerve of the eye, for example, differs from the nerves of touch only in the degree of its sensibility.

It is imagined that impressions, thus differing in kind, are carried along the nerves to the sensorium, and presented to the mind; and that the mind, by the same nerves which receive sensation, sends out the mandate of the will to the moving parts of the body.

It is further imagined, that there is a set of nerves, called vital nerves, which are less strictly connected with the sensorium, or which have upon them knots, cutting off the course of sensation, and thereby excluding the vital motions from the government of the will.

This appears sufficiently simple and consistent, until we begin to examine anatomically the structure of the brain, and course of the nerves,—then all is confusion: the divisions and subdivisions of the brain, the circuitous course of nerves, their intricate connections, their separation and re-union, are puzzling in the last degree, and are indeed considered as things inscrutable. Thus it is, that he who knows the parts the best, is most in a maze, and he who knows least of anatomy, sees least inconsistency in the commonly received opinion.

In opposition to these opinions, I have to offer reasons for believing, That the cerebrum and cerebellum are different in function as in form; That the parts of the cerebrum have different functions; and that the nerves which we trace in the body are not single nerves possessing various powers, but bundles of different nerves, whose filaments are united for the convenience of distribution, but which are distinct in office, as they are in origin from the brain:

That the external organs of the senses have the matter of the nerves adapted to receive certain impressions, while the corresponding organs of the brain are put in activity by the external excitement: That the idea or perception is according to the part of the brain to which the nerve is attached, and that each organ has a certain limited number of changes to be wrought upon it by the external impression:

That the nerves of sense, the nerves of motion, and the vital nerves, are distinct through their whole course, though they seem sometimes united in one bundle; and that they depend for their attributes on the organs of the brain to which they are severally attached.

The view which I have to present, will serve to show why there are divisions, and many distinct parts in the brain: why some nerves are simple in their origin and distribution, and others intricate beyond description. It will explain the apparently accidental connection between the twigs of nerves. It will do away the difficulty of conceiving how sensation and volition should be the operation of the same nerve at the same moment. It will show how a nerve may lose one property, and retain another; and it will give an interest to the labours of the anatomist in tracing the nerves.

When in contemplating the structure of the eye we say, how admirably it is adapted to the laws of light! we use language which implies a partial, and consequently an erroneous view. And the philosopher takes not a more enlarged survey of nature when he declares how curiously the laws of light are adapted to the constitution of the eye.

This creation, of which we are a part, has not been formed in parts. The organ of vision, and the matter or influence carried to the organ, and the qualities of bodies with which we are acquainted through it, are parts of a system great beyond our imperfect comprehension, formed as it should seem at once in wisdom; not pieced together like the work of human ingenuity.

When this whole was created, (of which the remote planetary system, as well as our bodies, and the objects more familiar to our observation, are but parts), the mind was placed in a body not merely suited to its residence, but in circumstances to be moved by the materials around it; and the capacities of the mind, and the powers of the organs, which are as a medium betwixt the mind and the external world, have an original constitution framed in relation to the qualities of things.

It is admitted that neither bodies nor the images of bodies enter the brain. It is indeed impossible to believe that colour can be conveyed along a nerve; or the vibration in which we suppose sound to consist can be retained in the brain: but we can conceive, and have reason to believe, that an impression is made upon the organs of the outward senses when we see, or hear, or taste.

In this inquiry it is most essential to observe, that while each organ of sense is provided with a capacity of receiving certain changes to be played upon it, as it were, yet each is utterly incapable of receiving the impressions destined for another organ of sensation.

It is also very remarkable that an impression made on two different nerves of sense, though with the same instrument, will produce two distinct sensations; and the ideas resulting will only have relation to the organ affected.

As the announcing of these facts forms a natural introduction to the Anatomy of the Brain, which I am about to deliver, I shall state them more fully.

There are four kinds of Papillæ on the tongue, but with two of those only we have to do at present. Of these, the Papillæ of one kind form the seat of the sense of taste; the other Papillæ (more numerous and smaller) resemble the extremities of the nerves in the common skin, and are the organs of touch in the tongue. When I take a sharp steel point, and touch one of *these* Papillæ, I feel the sharpness. The sense of *touch* informs me of the shape of the instrument. When I touch a Papilla of taste, I have no sensation similar to the former. I do not know that a point touches the tongue, but I am sensible to a metallic taste, and the sensation passes backward on the tongue.

In the operation of couching the cataract, the pain of piercing the retina with a needle is not so great as that which proceeds from a grain of sand under the eyelid. And although the derangement of the stomach sometimes marks the injury of an organ so delicate, yet the pain is occasioned by piercing the outward coat, not by the affection of the expanded nerve of vision.

If the sensation of light were conveyed to us by the retina, the organ of vision, in consequence of that organ being as much more sensible than the surface of the body as the impression of light is more delicate than that pressure which gives us the sense of touch; what would be the feelings of a man subjected to an operation in which a needle were pushed through the nerve. Life could not bear so great a pain.

But there is an occurrence during this operation on the eye which will direct us to the truth: when the needle pierces the eye, the patient has the sensation of a spark of fire before the eye.

This fact is corroborated by experiments made on the eye. When the eye-ball is pressed on the side, we perceive various coloured light. Indeed the mere effect of a blow on the head might inform us, that sensation depends on the exercise of the organ affected, not on the impression conveyed to the external organ; for by the vibration caused by the blow, the ears ring, and the eye flashes light, while there is neither light nor sound present.

It may be said, that there is here no proof of the sensation being in the brain more than in the external organ of sense. But when the nerve of a stump is touched, the pain is as if in the amputated extremity. If it be still said that this is no proper example of a peculiar sense existing without its external organ, I offer the following example: Qŭando penis glandem exedat ŭlcŭs, et nihil nisi granulatio maneat, ad extremam tamen nervi pudicæ partem ubi terminatŭr sensus supersunt, et exquisitissima sensŭs gratificatio.

If light, pressure, galvanism, or electricity produce vision, we must conclude that the idea in the mind is the result of an action excited in the eye or in the brain, not of anything received, though caused by an impression from without. The operations of the mind are confined not by the limited nature of things created, but by the limited number of our organs of sense. By induction we know that things exist which yet are not brought under the operation of the senses. When we have never known the operation of one of the organs of the five senses, we can never know the ideas pertaining to that sense; and what would be the effect on our minds, even constituted as they now are, with a superadded organ of sense, no man can distinctly imagine.

As we are parts of the creation, so God has bound us to the material world by this law of our nature, that it shall require excitement from without, and an operation produced by the action of things external to rouse our faculties: But that once brought into activity, the organs can be put in exercise by the mind, and be made to minister to the memory and imagination, and all the faculties of the soul.

I shall hereafter shew, that the operations of the mind are seated in the great mass of the cerebrum, while the parts of the brain to which the nerves of sense tend, strictly form the seat of the sensation, being the internal organs of sense. These organs are operated upon in two directions. They receive the impression from without, as from the eye and ear: and as their action influences the operations of the brain producing perception, so are they brought into action and suffer changes similar to that which they experience from external pressure by the operation of the will; or, as I am now treating of the subject anatomically, by the operation of the great mass of the brain upon them.

In all regulated actions of the muscles we must acknowledge that they are influenced through the same nerves, by the same operation of the sensorium. Now the operations of the body are as nice and curious, and as perfectly regulated before Reason has sway, as they are at any time after, when the muscular frame might be supposed to be under the guidance of sense and reason. Instinctive motions are the operations of the same organs, the brain and nerves and muscles, which minister to reason and volition in our mature years. When the young of any animal turns to the nipple, directed by the sense of smelling, the same operations are performed, and through the same means, as afterwards when we make an effort to avoid what is noxious, or desire and move towards what is agreeable.

The operations of the brain may be said to be threefold: 1. The frame of the body is endowed with the characters of life, and the vital parts held together as one system through the operation of the brain and nerves; and the secret operations of the vital organs suffer the controul of the brain, though we are unconscious of the thousand delicate operations which are every instant going on in the body. 2. In the second place, the instinctive motions which precede the developement of the intellectual faculties are performed through the brain and nerves. 3. In the last place, the operation of the senses in rouzing the faculties of the mind, and the exercise of the mind over the moving parts of the body, is through the brain and nerves. The first of these is perfect in nature, and independent of the mind. The second is a prescribed

and limited operation of the instrument of thought and agency.
The last begins by imperceptible degrees, and has no limit in
extent and variety. It is that to which all the rest is subservient,
the end being the calling into activity and the sustaining of an
intellectual being.

Thus we see that in as far as is necessary to the great system,
the operation of the brain, nerves, and muscles are perfect from
the beginning; and we are naturally moved to ask, Might not the
operations of the mind have been thus perfect and spontaneous
from the beginning as well as slowly excited into action by outward impressions? Then man would have been an insulated being,
not only cut off from the inanimate world around him, but from
his fellows; he would have been an individual, not part of a
whole. That he may have a motive and a spring to action, and
suffer pain and pleasure, and become an intelligent being, an-
swerable for his action,—sensation is made to result from external
impression, and reason and passion to come from the experience
of good and evil; first as they are in reference to his corporeal
frame, and finally as they belong to the intellectual privations
and enjoyments.

The brain is a mass of soft matter, in part of a white colour, and
generally striated; in part of a grey or cineritious colour having no
fibrous appearance. It has grand divisions and subdivisions: and
as the forms exist before the solid bone incloses the brain; and as
the distinctions of parts are equally observable in animals whose
brain is surrounded with fluid, they evidently are not accidental,
but are a consequence of internal structure; or in other words
they have a correspondence with distinctions in the uses of the
parts of the brain.

On examining the grand divisions of the brain we are forced to
admit that there are four brains. For the brain is divided longi-
tudinally by a deep fissure; and the line of distinction can even be
traced where the sides are united in substance. Whatever we
observe on one side has a corresponding part on the other; and
an exact resemblance and symmetry is preserved in all the lateral
divisions of the brain. And so, if we take the proof of anatomy, we
must admit that as the nerves are double, and the organs of sense

double, so is the brain double; and every sensation conveyed to the brain is conveyed to the two lateral parts; and the operations performed must be done in both lateral portions at the same moment.

I speak of the lateral divisions of the brain being distinct brains combined in function, in order the more strongly to mark the distinction betwixt the anterior and posterior grand divisions. Betwixt the lateral parts there is a strict resemblance in form and substance: each principal part is united by transverse tracts of medullary matter; and there is every provision for their acting with perfect sympathy. On the contrary, the *cerebrum*, the anterior grand division, and the *cerebellum* the posterior grand division, have slight and indirect connection. In form and division of parts, and arrangement of white and grey matter, there is no resemblance. There is here nothing of that symmetry and correspondence of parts which is so remarkable betwixt the right and left portions.

I have found evidence that the vascular system of the cerebellum may be affected independently of the vessels of the cerebrum. I have seen the whole surface of the cerebellum studded with spots of extravasated blood as small as pin heads, so as to be quite red, while no mark of disease was upon the surface of the cerebrum. The action of vessels it is needless to say is under the influence of the parts to which they go; and in this we have a proof of a distinct state of activity in the cerebrum and cerebellum.

From these facts, were there no others, we are entitled to conclude, that in the operations excited in the brain there cannot be such sympathy or corresponding movement in the cerebrum and cerebellum as there is betwixt the lateral portions of the cerebrum; that the anterior and posterior grand divisions of the brain perform distinct offices.

In examining this subject further, we find, when we compare the relative magnitude of the cerebrum to the other parts of the brain in man and in brutes, that in the latter the cerebrum is much smaller, having nothing of the relative magnitude and importance which in man it bears to the other parts of the nervous system; signifying that the cerebrum is the seat of those qualities of mind which distinguish man. We may observe also that the posterior grand division, or *cerebellum* remains more permanent in form: while the cerebrum changes in conformity to the organs of sense, or the endowments of the different classes of animals. In the inferior animals, for example, where there are two external organs of the same sense, there is to be found two distinct corresponding portions of cerebrum, while the cerebellum corresponds with the frame of the body.

In thinking of this subject, it is natural to expect that we should be able to put the matter to proof by experiment. But how is this to be accomplished, since any experiment direct upon the brain itself must be difficult, if not impossible?—I took this view of the subject. The *medulla spinalis* has a central division, and also a distinction into anterior and posterior fasciculi, corresponding with the anterior and posterior portions of the brain. Further we can trace down the crura of the *cerebrum* into the anterior fasciculus of the spinal marrow, and the crura of the *cerebellum* into the posterior fasciculus. I thought that here I might have an opportunity of touching the *cerebellum*, as it were, through the posterior portion of the spinal marrow, and the cerebrum by the anterior portion. To this end I made experiments which, though they were not conclusive, encouraged me in the view that I had taken.

I found that injury done to the anterior portion of the spinal marrow, convulsed the animal more certainly than injury done to the posterior portion; but I found it difficult to make the experiment without injuring both portions.

Next considering that the spinal nerves have a double root, and being of opinion that the properties of the nerves are derived from their connections with the parts of the brain, I thought that I had an opportunity of putting my opinion to the test of experiment, and of proving at the same time that nerves of different endowments were in the same cord, and held together by the same sheath.

On laying bare the roots of the spinal nerves, I found that I could cut across the posterior fasciculus of nerves, which took its origin from the posterior portion of the spinal marrow without convulsing the muscles of the back; but that on touching the anterior fasciculus with the point of the knife, the muscles of the back were immediately convulsed.

Such were my reasons for concluding that the cerebrum and the cerebellum were parts distinct in function, and that every nerve possessing a double function obtained that by having a double root. I now saw the meaning of the double connection of the nerves with the spinal marrow; and also the cause of that seeming intricacy in the connections of nerves throughout their course, which were not double at their origins.

The spinal nerves being double, and having their roots in the spinal marrow, of which a portion comes from the cerebrum and a portion from the cerebellum, they convey the attributes of both grand divisions of the brain to every part; and therefore the distribution of such nerves is simple, one nerve supplying its destined part. But the nerves which come directly from the brain, come from parts of the brain which vary in operation; and in order to bestow different qualities on the parts to which the nerves are distributed, two or more nerves must be united in their course or at their final destination. Hence it is that the 1st nerve must have branches of the 5th united with it: hence the *portio dura* of the 7th pervades everywhere the bones of the cranium to unite with the extended branches of the 5th: hence the union of the 3rd and 5th in the orbit: hence the 9th and 5th are both sent to the tongue: hence it is, in short, that no part is sufficiently supplied by one single nerve, unless that nerve be a nerve of the spinal marrow, and have a double root, a connection (however remotely) with both the cerebrum and cerebellum.

Such nerves as are single in their origin from the spinal marrow will be found either to unite in their course with some other nerve, or to be such as are acknowledged to be peculiar in their operation.

The 8th nerve is from the portion of the *medulla oblongata* which belongs to the cerebellum: the 9th nerve comes from the portion which belongs to the cerebrum. The first is a nerve of the class called Vital nerves, controuling secretly the operation of the body; the last is the Motor nerve of the tongue, and is an instrument of volition. Now the connections formed by the 8th nerve in its course to the viscera are endless; it seems nowhere sufficient for the entire purpose of a nerve; for everywhere it is accompanied by others, and the 9th passes to the tongue, which is already profusely supplied by the 5th.

Understanding the origin of the nerves in the brain to be the source of their powers, we look upon the connections formed betwixt distant nerves, and upon the combination of nerves in their passage, with some interest; but without this the whole is an unmeaning tissue. Seeing the seeming irregularity in one subject, we say it is accident; but finding that the connections never vary, we say only that it is strange, until we come to understand the necessity of nerves being combined in order to bestow distinct qualities on the parts to which they are sent.

The *cerebellum* when compared with the *cerebrum* is simple in its form. It has no internal tubercles or masses of cineritious matter in it. The medullary matter comes down from the cineritious cortex, and forms the *crus;* and the crus runs into union with the same process from the cerebrum; and they together form the *medulla spinalis,* and are continued down into the spinal marrow; and these crura or processes afford double origin to the double nerves of the spine. The nerves proceeding from the Crus Cerebelli go everywhere (in seeming union with those from the Crus Cerebri); they unite the body together, and controul the actions of the bodily frame; and especially govern the operation of the viscera necessary to the continuance of life.

In all animals having a nervous system, the *cerebellum* is apparent, even though there be no *cerebrum.* The cerebrum is seen in such tribes of animals as have organs of sense, and it is seen to be near the eyes, or principal organ of sense; and sometimes it is quite separate from the *cerebellum.*

The cerebrum I consider as the grand organ by which the mind is united to the body. Into it all the nerves from the external organs of the senses enter; and from it all the nerves which are agents of the will pass out.

If this be not at once obvious, it proceeds only from the circumstance that the nerves take their origin from the different parts of the brain; and while those nerves are considered as simple cords, this circumstance stands opposed to the conclusion which otherways would be drawn. A nerve having several roots, implies that it propagates its sensation to the brain generally. But when we find that the several roots are distinct in their endowments, and are in respect to office distinct nerves; then the conclusion is unavoidable, that the portions of the brain are distinct organs of different functions.

To arrive at any understanding of the internal parts of the cerebrum, we must keep in view the relation of the nerves, and must class and distinguish the nerves, and follow them into its substance. If all ideas originate in the mind from external impulse, how can we better investigate the structure of the brain than by following the nerves, which are the means of communication betwixt the brain and the outward organs of the senses?

The nerves of sense, the olfactory, the optic, the auditory, and the gustatory nerve, are traced backwards into certain tubercles or convex bodies in the base of the brain. And I may say, that the nerves of sense either form tubercles before entering the brain, or they enter into those convexities in the base of the *cerebrum*. These convexities are the constituent parts of the cerebrum, and are in all animals necessary parts of the organs of sense: for as certainly as we discover an animal to have an external organ of sense, we find also a medullary tubercle; whilst the superiority of animals in intelligence is shown by the greater magnitude of the hemispheres or upper part of the cerebrum.

The convex bodies which are seated in the lower part of the cerebrum, and into which the nerves of sense enter, have extensive connection with the hemispheres on their upper part. From the medullary matter of the hemispheres, again, there pass down, converging to the crura, Striæ, which is the medullary matter taking upon it the character of a nerve; for from the Crura Cerebri, or its prolongation in the anterior Fasciculi of the spinal marrow, go off the nerves of motion.

But with these nerves of motion which are passing outward there are nerves going inwards; nerves from the surfaces of the body; nerves of touch; and nerves of peculiar sensibility, having their seat in the body or viscera. It is not improbable that the tracts of cineritious matter which we observe in the course of the medullary matter of the brain, are the seat of such peculiar sensibilities; the organs of certain powers which seem resident in the body.

As we proceed further in the investigation of the function of the brain, the discussion becomes more hypothetical. But surely physiologists have been mistaken in supposing it necessary to prove sensibility in those parts of the brain which they are to suppose the seat of the intellectual operations. We are not to expect the same phenomena to result from the cutting or tearing of the brain as from the injury to the nerves. The function of the one is to transmit sensation; the other has a higher operation. The nature of the organs of sense is different; the sensibilities of the parts of the body are very various. If the needle piercing the retina during the operation of couching gives no remarkable pain, except in touching the common coats of the eye, ought we to imagine that the seat of the higher operations of the mind should, when injured, exhibit the same effects with the irritation of a nerve? So far therefore from thinking the parts of the brain which are insensible, to be parts inferior (as every part has its use), I should even from this be led to imagine that they had a higher office. And if there be certain parts of the brain which are insensible, and other parts which being injured shake the animal with convulsions exhibiting phenomena similar to those of a wounded nerve, it seems to follow that the latter parts which are endowed with sensibility like the nerves are similar to them in function and use; while the parts of the brain which possess no such sensibility are different in function and organization from the nerves, and have a distinct and higher operation to perform.

If in examining the apparent structure of the brain, we find a part consisting of white medullary Striæ and fasciculated like a nerve, we should conclude that as the use of a nerve is to transmit sensation, not to perform any more peculiar function, such tracts of matter are media of communication, connecting the parts of the brain; rather than the brain itself performing the more peculiar functions. On the other hand, if masses are found in the brain unlike the matter of the nerve, and which yet occupy a place guarded as an organ of importance, we may presume that such parts have a use different from that of merely conveying sensation; we may rather look upon such parts as the seat of the higher powers.

Again, if those parts of the brain which are directly connected with the nerves, and which resemble them in structure, give pain when injured, and occasion convulsion to the animal as the nerves do when they are injured; and if on the contrary such parts as are more remote from the nerves, and if a different structure, produce no such effect when injured, we may conclude, that the office of the latter parts is more allied to the intellectual operations, less to mere sensation.

I have found at different times all the internal parts of the brain diseased without loss of sense; but I have never seen disease general on the surfaces of the hemispheres without derangement or oppression of the mind during the patient's life. In the case of derangement of mind, falling into lethargy and stupidity, I have constantly found the surface of the hemispheres dry and preternaturally firm, the membrane separating from it with unusual facility.

If I be correct in this view of the subject, then the experiments which have been made upon the brain tend to confirm the conclusions which I should be inclined to draw from strict anatomy; viz. that the cineritious and superficial parts of the brain are the seat of the intellectual functions. For it is found that the surface of the brain is totally insensible, but that the deep and medullary part being wounded the animal is convulsed and pained.

At first it is difficult to comprehend, how the part to which every sensation is referred, and by means of which we become acquainted with the various sensations, can itself be insensible; but the consideration of the wide difference of function betwixt a part destined to receive impressions, and a part which is the seat of intellect, reconciles us to the phenomenon. It would be rather strange to find, that there were no distinction exhibited in experiments on parts evidently so different in function as the organs of the senses, the nerves, and the brain. Whether there be a difference in the matter of the nervous system, or a distinction in organization, is of little importance to our enquiries, when it is proved that their essential properties are different, though their union and co-operation be necessary to the completion of their function—the developement of the faculties by impulse from external matter.

All ideas originate in the brain: the operation producing them is the remote effect of an agitation or impression on the extremities of the nerves of sense; directly they are consequences of a change or operation in the proper organ of the sense which constitutes a part of the brain, and over these organs, once brought into action by external impulse, the mind has influence. It is provided, that the extremities of the nerves of the senses shall be susceptible each of certain qualities in matter; and betwixt the impression of the outward sense, as it may be called, and the exercise of the internal organ, there is established a connection by which the ideas excited have a permanent correspondence with the qualities of bodies which surround us.

From the cineritious matter, which is chiefly external, and forming the surface of the cerebrum; and from the grand center of medullary matter of the cerebrum, what are called the *crura* descend. These are fasciculated processes of the cerebrum, from which go off the nerves of motion, the nerves governing the muscular frame. Through the nerves of sense, the *sensorium* receives impressions, but the will is expressed through the medium of the nerves of motion. The secret operations of the bodily frame, and the connections which unite the parts of the body into a system, are through the cerebellum and nerves proceeding from it.

* * *

The work of Bell and Magendie is especially pertinent to the history of perception because it emphasizes separation of distinct elements (in this case neural elements) from an apparently uniform whole. This emphasis on separation has both particular and general significance. In particular, it reinforces the common sense assumption of the independence of the sensory and motor systems. Only toward the end of the century, most directly in the revolutionary article by John Dewey on the reflex arc concept (see Chapter 6), is any dissatisfaction expressed with what seems a logically correct and anatomically compelling distinction between the sensory and the motoric, between experience and action. The case for the mutual interdependence of the two systems has been restated in more recent times by Werner and Wapner in their "sensory-tonic field theory" of perception.*

In its more general implications, the work of Bell and Magendie suggests looking for, or at least hypothesizing, separate neural elements for each mode of experience and perhaps for each attribute within a mode. Further, if the neural substrate of experience is comprised of numerous independent types of elements, then experience itself must also be so comprised. Just as a peripheral nerve seems, but on close examination really is not, homogenous, so too experience, which naively appears uniform, whole, all-of-a-piece, is really constructed from separate elements whose identity can be discerned by taking the proper "dissecting" attitude. Thus, the work of Bell and Magendie, of great significance in its own right, also presages, and serves as a model for, the analytic approach that characterizes most of nineteenth century thinking about perception and, indeed, about all of psychology.

The broad implications of the Bell-Magendie Law are manifest in the next two passages. First, the physiologist Müller proposes a solution, in the form of a set of postulates, to the problem of the neural basis for qualitative differences in sensory experience. These postulates make up the Doctrine of Specific Nerve Energies, for which Müller is so justly famous. It should be noted that two alternative bases for qualitative differences in experience were offered by Müller—differences in the nature of the nerve impulse or differences in the locus of termination of the

---

* H. Werner and S. Wapner. Sensory-tonic field theory of perception. *J. Personal.*, 1949, **18**, 88–107.

neural activity. At present it is the latter alternative that is the generally accepted solution.

When Müller's doctrine was published, very little was actually known about the mechanism of neural transmission, about nerve histology, and about the structural and functional organization of the brain. The "neurone doctrine," developed by Waldeyer, Cajal, and others, which specified the neurone, a single, structurally independent cell, as the basic unit of nervous transmission, was not to be promulgated until later in the century. And the fundamental details of the nerve impulse, its electrical nature, speed, and other characteristics had not yet been worked out. Thus, there was little reason for Müller to reject the still plausible hypothesis that each nerve had its own characteristic and therefore identifying "energy."

Moreover, the hypothesis of localization of function within the brain was quite controversial at this time. Partly because of a lack of good evidence, and partly because of theologically derived bias, the prevailing sentiment considered the brain to be a unified whole, analogous to the unified soul which it encased. In addition, the notion of localization of function within the brain was in considerable disfavor because one of its chief proponents, Gall, the founder of Phrenology, was himself held in disrepute by a large part of the scientific community of Europe.

However, as more and more evidence was accumulated, it became clear that the impulses generated by the nerves serving the various sense modalities are not qualitatively distinct, though they might vary quantitatively, as in speed and amplitude. It also became apparent that the brain *is* organized into functionally distinct regions (for example, there is a "visual area" located in the occipital lobe of the cerebral cortex), and indeed that these gross areas of the brain are themselves finely organized, structurally and functionally.

Thus, of Müller's two alternative solutions to the problem of qualitative differences among the various sense modalities, the one postulating "specific nerve energies" must be rejected on the basis of present knowledge; more likely to be grossly correct is the alternative that points to differences in the terminal locus of the neural activity arising in the receptor organs.

Johannes Müller

Of the Senses

The senses, by virtue of the peculiar properties of their several nerves, make us acquainted with the states of our own body, and they also inform us of the qualities and changes of external nature, as far as these give rise to changes in the condition of the nerves. Sensation is a property common to all the senses; but the kind, ("*modus,*") of sensation is different in each: thus we have the sensations of light, of sound, of taste, of smell, and of feeling or touch. By feeling, or touch, we understand the peculiar kind of sensation of which the ordinary sensitive nerves generally—as, the nervus trigeminus, vagus, glossopharyngeus, and the spinal nerves,—are susceptible; the sensations of itching, of pleasure and pain, of heat and cold, and those excited by the act of touch in its more limited sense, are varieties of this mode of sensation. That which through the medium of our senses is actually perceived by the sensorium, is indeed merely a property or change of condition of our nerves; but the imagination and reason are ready to interpret the modifications in the state of the nerves produced by external influences as properties of the external bodies themselves. This mode of regarding sensations has become so habitual in the case of the senses which are more rarely affected by internal causes, that it is only on reflection that we perceive it to be erroneous. In the case of the sense of feeling or touch, on the contrary, where the peculiar sensations of the nerves per-

J. Müller. *Elements of physiology.* Translated by W. Baly. London: Taylor & Walton, Vol. I (1838); Vol. II (1842). The first German edition of *Handbuch der Physiologie des Menschen für Vorlesungen* was published by Hölscher in Coblenz between 1834 (5?) and 1840. This selection is taken from Vol. II, Book V, pp. 1059–1087 in the Baly translation.

ceived by the sensorium are excited as frequently by internal as by external causes, it is easily conceived that the feeling of pain or pleasure, for example, is a condition of the nerves, and not a property of the things which excite it. This leads us to the consideration of some general laws, a knowledge of which is necessary before entering on the physiology of the separate senses.

I. In the first place, it must be kept in mind that *external agencies can give rise to no kind of sensation which cannot also be produced by internal causes, exciting changes in the condition of our nerves.*

In the case of the sense of touch, this is at once evident. The sensations of the nerves of touch (or common sensibility) are those of cold and heat, pain and pleasure, and innumerable modifications of these, which are neither painful nor pleasurable, but yet have the same kind of sensation as their element, though not in an extreme degree. All these sensations are constantly being produced by internal causes in all parts of our body endowed with sensitive nerves; they may also be excited by causes acting from without, but external agencies are not capable of adding any new element to their nature. The sensations of the nerves of touch are therefore states or qualities proper to themselves, and merely rendered manifest by exciting causes external or internal. The sensation of smell also may be perceived independently of the application of any odorous substance from without, the nerve of smell being thrown by an internal cause into the condition requisite for the production of the sensation. This perception of the sensation of odours without an external exciting cause, though not of frequent occurrence, has been many times observed in persons of an irritable nervous system; and the sense of taste is probably subject to the same affection, although it would always be difficult to determine whether the taste might not be owing to a change in the qualities of the saliva or mucus of the mouth; the sensation of nausea, however, which belongs to the sensations of taste, is certainly very often perceived as the result of a merely internal affection of the nerves. The sensations of the sense of vision, namely colour, light, and darkness, are also perceived independently of all external exciting cause. In the state of the most perfect freedom from excitement, the optic nerve has no other sensation than that of darkness. The excited condition of the nerve is manifested, even while the eyes are closed, by the appearance of light, or luminous flashes, which are mere sensations of the nerve, and not owing to the presence of any matter of light, and consequently are not capable of illuminating any surrounding objects. Every one is aware how common it is to see bright colours while the eyes are closed, particularly in the morning when the irritability of the nerves is still considerable. These phenomena are very frequent in children after waking from sleep. Through the sense of vision, therefore, we receive from external nature no impressions which we may not also experience from internal excitement of our nerves; and it is evident that a person blind from infancy in consequence of opacity of the transparent media of the eye, must have a perfect internal conception of light and colours, provided the retina and optic nerve be free from lesion. The prevalent notions with regard to the wonderful sensations supposed to be experienced by persons blind from birth when their sight is restored by operation, are exaggerated and incorrect. The elements of the sensation of vision, namely the sensations of light, colour, and darkness, must have been previously as well known to such persons as to those of whom the sight has always been perfect. If, moreover, we imagine a man to be from his birth surrounded merely by external objects destitute of all variety of colours, so that he could never receive the impressions of colours from without, it is evident that the sense of vision might nevertheless have been no less perfect in him than in other men; for light and colours are innate endowments of his nature, and require merely a stimulus to render them manifest.

The sensations of hearing also are excited as well by internal as by external causes; for, whenever the auditory nerve is in a state of excitement, the sensations peculiar to it, as the sounds of ringing, humming, &c. are perceived. It is by such sensations that the diseases of the auditory nerve manifest themselves; and, even in less grave transient affections of the nervous system, the sensations of humming and ringing in the ears afford evidence that the sense of hearing participates in the disturbance.

No further proof is wanting to show, that external influences give rise in our senses to no other sensations, than those which may be excited in the corresponding nerves by internal causes.

II. *The same internal cause excites in the different senses different sensations;—in each sense the sensations peculiar to it.*

One uniform internal cause acting on all the nerves of the senses in the same manner, is the accumulation of blood in the capillary vessels of the nerve, as in congestion and inflammation. This uniform cause excites in the retina, while the eyes are closed, the sensation of light and luminous flashes; in the auditory nerve, humming and ringing sounds; and in the nerves of feeling, the sensation of pain. In the same way, also, a narcotic substance introduced into the blood excites in the nerves of each sense peculiar symptoms; in the optic nerves the appearance of luminous sparks before the eyes; in the auditory nerves, "tinnitus aurium;" and in the common sensitive nerves the sensation of ants creeping over the surface.

III. *The same external cause also gives rise to different sensations in each sense, according to the special endowments of its nerve.*

The mechanical influence of a blow, concussion, or pressure excites, for example, in the eye the sensation of light and colours. It is well known that by exerting pressure upon the eye, when the eyelids are closed, we can give rise to the appearance of a luminous circle; by more gentle pressure the appearance of colours may be produced, and one colour may be made to change to another. Children, waking from sleep before daylight, frequently amuse themselves with these phenomena. The light thus produced has no existence external to the optic nerve, it is merely a sensation excited in it. However strongly we press upon the eye in the dark, so as to give rise to the appearance of luminous flashes, these flashes, being merely sensations, are incapable of illuminating external objects. Of this any one may easily convince himself by experiment. I have in repeated trials never been able, by means of these luminous flashes in the eye, to recognise in the dark the nearest objects, or to see them better than before; nor could another person, while I produced by pressure on my eye the appearance of brilliant flashes, perceive in it the slightest trace of real light. . . .

The supposed emission of light by the eyes of animals has been already discussed in the Prolegomena. . . . It is not, *à priori*, contrary to known laws, to suppose that the nerves of animals may develope luminous matter; and since we have in the retina of the eye an opportunity which we have nowhere else, of observing a nerve through transparent media without inflicting any injury on the animal, it would be here that such a phenomenon would be best observed. The fact of light being developed by the retina and nerves, even were it proved by experiment, would not, however, influence the explanation of the appearance of light produced in the eye by internal causes.

A mechanical influence excites also peculiar sensations of the auditory nerve; at all events, it has become a common saying, "to give a person what will make his ears ring," or "what will make his eyes flash fire," or "what will make him feel;" so that the same cause, a blow, produces in the nerves of hearing, sight, and feeling, the different sensations proper to these senses. It has not become a part of common language that a blow shall be given which will excite the sense of smell, or of taste; nor would such sayings be correct; yet mechanical irritation of the soft palate, of the epiglottis and root of the tongue, excites the sensation of nausea. The action of sonorous bodies on the organ of hearing is entirely mechanical. A sudden mechanical impulse of the air upon the organ of hearing produces the sensation of a report of different degrees of intensity according to the violence of the impulse, just as an impulse upon the organ of vision gives rise to the sensation of light. If the action of the mechanical cause on the organ of hearing be of continued duration, the sound is also continued; and when caused by a rapid succession of uniform impulses, or vibrations, it has a musical character. . . . If we admit that the matter of light acts on bodies by mechanical oscillation, (the undulation theory,) we shall have another example of a mechanical influence, producing different effects on different senses. These undulations, which produce in the eye the sensation of light, have no such effect on other senses; but in the nerves of feeling they produce the sensation of warmth.

The stimulus of electricity may serve as a second example, of a uniform cause giving rise in different nerves of sense to different sensations. A single pair of plates of different metals applied so as to include the eye within the circle, excites the sensation of a bright flash of light when the person experimented upon is in a dark room; and, even though the eye do not lie within the circle, if it be not distant from it,—as, for example, when one of the plates is applied to one of the eyelids, and the other to the interior of the mouth,—the same effect will be produced, owing to a part of the current of electricity being diverted to the eye. A more intense electric stimulus gives rise to more intense sensations of light. In the organ of hearing, electricity excites the sensation of sound. Volta states that, while his ears were included between the poles of a battery of forty pairs of plates, he heard a hissing and pulsatory sound, which continued as long as the circle was closed. Ritter perceived a sound like that of the fiddle G at the moment of the closure of the galvanic circle.

The electricity of friction, developed by the electrical machine, excites in the olfactory nerves the odour of phosphorus. The application of plates of different metals to the tongue, gives rise to an acid or a saline taste, according to the length of the plates which are applied one above, and the other beneath the tongue. The facts detailed with regard to the other senses are sufficient to show that these latter phenomena cannot be attributed to decomposition of the salts of the saliva.

The effects of the action of electricity on the nerves of common sensation or feeling, are neither the sensation of light, of sound, of smell, nor of taste, but those proper to the nerves of feeling, namely, the sensations of pricking, of a blow, &c.

Chemical influences also probably produce different effects on different nerves of sense. We have, of course, but few facts illustrating their action on these nerves; but we know that in the sensitive nerves of the skin they excite the different kinds of common sensation,—as the sensations of burning, pain, and heat; in the organ of taste, sensations of taste; and, when volatile, in the nerves of smell, the sensations of odours. Without the infliction of great injury on the textures, it is impossible to apply chemical agents to the nerves of the higher senses, sight and hearing, except through the medium of the blood. Chemical substances introduced into the blood act on every nerve of sense, and excite in each a manifestation of its properties. Hence the internal sensations of light and sound, which are well known to result from the action of narcotics.

IV. *The peculiar sensations of each nerve of sense can be excited by several distinct causes internal and external.*

The facts on which this statement is founded, have been already mentioned; for we have seen that the sensation of light in the eye is excited:

1. By the undulations or emanations which from their action on the eye are called light, although they have many other actions than this; for instance, they effect chemical changes, and are the means of maintaining the organic processes in plants.

2. By mechanical influences; as concussion, or a blow.

3. By electricity.

4. By chemical agents, such as narcotics, digitalis, &c. which, being absorbed into the blood, give rise to the appearance of luminous sparks, &c. before the eyes independently of any external cause.

5. By the stimulus of the blood in the state of congestion.

The sensation of sound may be excited in the auditory nerve:

1. By mechanical influences, namely, by the vibrations of sonorous bodies imparted to the organ of hearing through the intervention of media capable of propagating them.

2. By electricity.

3. By chemical influences taken into the circulation; such as the narcotics, or alterantia nervina.

4. By the stimulus of the blood.

The sensation of odours may be excited in the olfactory nerves:

1. By chemical influences of a volatile nature,—odorous substances.

2. By electricity.

The sensation of taste may be produced:

1. By chemical influences acting on the gustatory nerves either from without or through the medium of the blood; for, according to Magendie, dogs taste milk injected into their blood-vessels, and begin to lap with their tongue.

2. By electricity.

3. By mechanical influences; for we must refer to taste the sensation of nausea produced by mechanically irritating the velum palati, epiglottis, and root of the tongue.

The sensations of the nerves of touch or feeling are excited:

1. By mechanical influences; as sonorous vibrations, and contact of any kind.

2. By chemical influences.

3. By heat.

4. By electricity.

5. By the stimulus of the blood.

V. *Sensation consists in the sensorium receiving through the medium of the nerves, and as the result of the action of an external cause, a knowledge of certain qualities or conditions, not of external bodies, but of the nerves of sense themselves; and these qualities of the nerves of sense are in all different, the nerve of each sense having its own peculiar quality or energy.*

The special susceptibility of the different nerves of sense for certain influences,—as of the optic nerve for light, of the auditory nerve for vibrations, and so on,—was formerly attributed to these nerves having each a specific irritability. But this hypothesis is evidently insufficient to explain all the facts. The nerves of the senses have assuredly a specific irritability for certain influences; for many stimuli, which exert a violent action upon one organ of sense, have little or no effect upon another: for example, light, or vibrations so infinitely rapid as those of light, act only on the nerves of vision and common sensation; slower vibrations, on the nerves of hearing and common sensation, but not upon those of vision; odorous substances only upon the olfactory nerves. The external stimuli must therefore be adapted to the organ of sense— must be "homogeneous:" thus light is the stimulus adapted to the nerve of vision; while vibrations of less rapidity, which act upon the auditory nerve, are not adapted to the optic nerve, or are indifferent to it; for, if the eye be touched with a tuning-fork while vibrating, a sensation of tremours is excited in the conjunctiva, but no sensation of light. We have seen, however, that one and the same stimulus, as electricity, will produce different sensations in the different nerves of the senses; all the nerves are susceptible of its action, but the sensations in all are different.

The same is the case with other stimuli, as chemical and mechanical influences. The hypothesis of a specific irritability of the nerves of the senses for certain stimuli, is therefore insufficient; and we are compelled to ascribe, with Aristotle, peculiar energies to each nerve,—energies which are vital qualities of the nerve, just as contractility is the vital property of muscle. The truth of this has been rendered more and more evident in recent times by the investigation of the so-called "subjective" phenomena of the senses by Elliot, Darwin, Ritter, Goethe, Purkinje, and Hjort. Those phenomena of the senses, namely, are now styled "subjective," which are produced, not by the usual stimulus adapted to the particular nerve of sense, but by others which do not usually act upon it. These important phenomena were long spoken of as "illusions of the senses," and have been regarded in an erroneous point of view; while they are really true actions of the senses, and must be studied as fundamental phenomena in investigations into their nature.

The sensation of sound, therefore, is the peculiar "energy" or "quality" of the auditory nerve; the sensation of light and colours that of the optic nerve; and so of the other nerves of sense. An exact analysis of what takes place in the production of a sensation would of itself have led to this conclusion. The sensations of heat and cold, for example, make us acquainted with the existence of the imponderable matter of caloric, or of peculiar vibrations in the vicinity of our nerves of feeling. But the nature of this caloric cannot be elucidated by sensation, which is in reality merely a particular state of our nerves; it must be learnt by the study of the physical properties of this agent, namely, of the laws of its radiation, its developement from the latent state, its property of combining with and producing expansion of other bodies, &c. All this again, however, does not explain the peculiarity of the sensation of warmth as a condition of the nerves. The simple fact devoid of all theory is this, that warmth, as a sensation, is produced whenever the matter of caloric acts upon the nerves of feeling; and that cold, as a sensation, results from this matter of caloric being abstracted from a nerve of feeling.

So, also, the sensation of sound is produced when a certain number of impulses or vibrations are imparted, within a certain time, to the auditory nerve: but sound, as we perceive it, is a very different thing from a succession of vibrations. The vibrations of a tuning-fork, which to the ear give the impression of sound, produce in a nerve of feeling or touch the sensation of tickling; something besides the vibrations must consequently be necessary for the production of the sensation of sound, and that something is possessed by the auditory nerve alone. Vision is to be regarded in the same manner. A difference in the intensity of the action of the imponderable agent, light, causes an inequality of sensation at different parts of the retina: whether this action consists in impulses or undulations, (the undulation theory,) or in an infinitely rapid current of imponderable matter, (the emanation theory,) is a question here of no importance. The sensation of moderate light is produced where the action of the imponderable agent on the retina is not intense; of bright light where its action is stronger, and of darkness or shade where the imponderable agent does not fall; and thus results a luminous image of determinate form according to the distribution of the parts of the retina differently acted on. Colour is also a property of the optic nerve; and, when excited by external light, arises from the peculiarity of the so-called coloured rays, or of the oscillations necessary for the production of the impression of colour,—a peculiarity, the nature of which is not at present known. The nerves of taste and smell are capable of being excited to an infinite variety of sensations by external causes; but each taste is due to a determinate condition of the nerve excited by the external cause; and it is ridiculous to say that the property of acidity is communicated to the sensorium by the nerve of taste, while the acid acts equally upon the nerves of feeling, though it excites there no sensation of taste.

The essential nature of these conditions of the nerves, by virtue of which they see light and hear sound,—the essential nature of sound as a property of the auditory nerve, and of light as a property of the optic nerve, of taste, of smell, and of feeling,—remains, like the ultimate causes of natural phenomena generally, a problem incapable of solution. Respecting the nature of the sensation of the colour "blue," for example, we can reason no farther; it is one of the many facts which mark the limits of our powers of mind. It would not advance the question to suppose, the peculiar sensations of the different senses excited by one and the same cause, to result from the propagation of vibrations of the nervous principle of different rapidity to the sensorium. Such an hypothesis, if at all tenable, would find its first application in accounting for the different sensations of which a single sense is susceptible; for example, in explaining how the sensorium receives the different impressions of blue, red, and yellow, or of an acute and a grave tone, or of painful and pleasurable sensations, or of the sensations of heat and cold, or of the tastes of bitter, sweet, and acid. It is only with this application that the hypothesis is worthy of regard: tones of different degrees of acuteness are certainly produced by vibrations of sonorous bodies of different degrees of rapidity; and a slight contact of a solid body, which singly excites in a nerve of common sensation merely the simple sensation of touch, produces in the same nerve when repeated rapidly, as the vibrations of a sonorous body, the feeling of tickling; so that possibly a pleasurable sensation, even when it arises from internal causes independently of external influences, is due to the rapidity of the vibrations of the nervous principle in the nerves of feeling.

It was perhaps from an obscure acquaintance with the phenomena of the sensation of light from internal causes, that even the older philosophers derived their imperfect idea of the essential part which the eye itself plays in the sensations of light and colour. Such an idea can evidently be traced in Plato's doctrine of vision in the Timaeus. . . .

Aristotle's treatise on dreams contains views in themselves more correct, and stated in a more scientific form. His explanation of spectral appearances as the result of internal actions of the sense of vision, is quite on a level with the present state of science. He adduces indeed the observation since made by Spinoza, that images seen during sleep can still be perceived in the organs of vision after waking; and the varying colours of the ocular spectra produced by gazing at the sun were well known to him.

In the present more perfect state of the different branches of natural science, which are studied separately, and in part independently of each other, it still remains a task, well deserving the labour it would cost, to test the theories of fundamental phenomena, more especially of those which interest different sciences, such as the actions of light upon organic beings. But this would be a task of extreme difficulty, requiring for its proper performance a critical examination of the various facts.

During recent years, philosophy has done little in this field of inquiry. The manifestation of different objects to each other cannot express the nature of light; that it renders objects visible to us depends merely on our having an organ of vision with vital properties. And in this way many other agents have the same power of rendering objects manifest: were we endowed with as delicate an organic re-agent for electricity as for light, electricity would have the same influence as light in rendering manifest the corporeal world.

From the foregoing considerations we have learnt most clearly that the nerves of the senses are not mere conductors of the properties of bodies to our sensorium, and that we are made acquainted with external objects merely by virtue of certain properties of our nerves, and of their faculty of being affected in a greater or less degree by external bodies. Even the sensation of touch in our hands makes us acquainted, not absolutely with the state of the surfaces of the body touched, but with changes produced in the parts of our body affected by the act of touch. By imagination and reason a mere sensation is interpreted as something quite different.

The accuracy of our discrimination by means of the senses depends on the different manner in which the conditions of our nerves are affected by different bodies; but the preceding considerations show us the impossibility that our senses can ever reveal to us the true nature and essence of the material world. In our intercourse with external nature it is always our own sensations that we become acquainted with, and from them we form conceptions of the properties of external objects, which may be relatively correct; but we can never submit the nature of the objects themselves to that immediate perception to which the states of the different parts of our own body are subjected in the sensorium.

VI. *The nerve of each sense seems to be capable of one determinate kind of sensation only, and not of those proper to the other organs of sense; hence one nerve of sense cannot take the place and perform the function of the nerve of another sense.*

The sensation of each organ of sense may be increased in intensity till it becomes pleasurable, or till it becomes disagreeable, without the specific nature of the sensation being altered, or converted into that of another organ of sense. The sensation of dazzling light is an unpleasant sensation of the organ of vision; harmony of colours, an agreeable one. Harmonious and discordant sounds are agreeable and disagreeable sensations of the organ of hearing. The organs of taste and smell have their pleasant and unpleasant tastes and odours; the organ of touch, its pleasurable and painful feelings. It appears, therefore, that, even in the most excited condition of an organ of sense, the sensation preserves its specific character. It is an admitted fact that the sensations of light, sound, taste, and odours, can be experienced only in their respective nerves; but in the case of common sensation this is not so evidently the case, for it is a question whether the sensation of pain may not be felt in the nerves of the higher senses,—whether, for example, violent irritation of the optic nerve may not give rise to the sensation of pain. This question is difficult of solution. There are filaments of the nerves of common sensation distributed in the nerves of the other organs of sense: the nostrils are supplied with nerves of common sensation from the second division of the nervus trigeminus in addition to the olfactory nerves; the tongue has common sensibility as well as taste, and may retain the one while it loses the other; the eye and organ of hearing likewise are similarly endowed.

To determine this question, it is necessary to institute experiments on the isolated nerves of special sense themselves. As far as such experiments have hitherto gone, they favour the view that the nerves of sense are susceptible of no other kind of sensation than that peculiar to each, and are not endowed with the faculty of common sensibility.

The olfactory nerves laid bare in the dog evince, when pricked, as Magendie observed, no sign of common sensibility; and the retina and optic nerve were also in Magendie's experiments insusceptible of pain from mechanical injury. On the other hand, it has been observed that the division of the optic nerve in extirpation of the eye was attended with the perception of a great light, a fact of which my friend M. Tourtual assured me from his own observation. The luminous rings seen when the eyes are suddenly turned to one side are facts of the same kind; they are the result of the mechanical stretching of the optic nerve. In many of the cases in which extirpation of the eye is indicated, the optic nerve is itself so changed in structure as to be no longer capable of sensation; consequently, the above phenomenon must not be expected to be constant in its occurrence. In two cases of extirpation of the eye, performed in Berlin, it was not perceived. I am not aware, however, that the division of the optic nerve was in these instances attended with more pain than the other parts of the operation; while the division of a common sensitive nerve of the same thickness is productive of the most rightful pain, and in animals calls forth a sudden and loud cry.

An impression upon one nerve of sense may, it is true, give rise by reflection through the intervention of the brain to other sensations; for example, the sound of scratching glass excited in the auditory nerve, produces the feeling of cold creeping over the surface, "horripilatio," in the nerves of common sensation. And in the same way a dazzling sensation of light in the optic nerve, may possibly give rise by reflection to a painful impression on the sensitive nerves of the orbit and ball of the eye; in this way we may, at all events, explain the painful sensations in the eye which follow the impression of a very bright light.

With respect to the sense of smell, it is evident that Magendie was deceived in ascribing the power of distinguishing odours to the nasal branches of the fifth nerve, after the destruction of the olfactory nerves; since the stimuli which he applied—for instance, acetic acid, liquor ammoniae, oil of lavender, and oil of dippel,— are themselves strong excitants of the common sensibility of the mucous membrane. In all accurately observed cases of absence of the olfactory nerves, the true sense of smell has been wanting.

No one can deny the possibility of the optic nerves influencing the nerves of the other senses, to the extent in which one nerve can act on another, through the medium of the brain. What an extensive affection of the nerves is seen in neuralgia! what manifold disturbances of the organs of sense result from a nervous condition which has its source in the viscera of the abdomen! How common in such cases are imperfection of vision, noises in the ears, &c.! although it is certain that much which is laid to the score of the abdomen has a much deeper source, namely, irritation of the spinal cord.

It is thus, also, that we must regard the sympathy of the optic nerve with the frontal branch of the fifth, and those cases of amaurosis observed to follow injury of the frontal nerve; though it would perhaps be more correct to explain such affections, which according to my experience are now but rarely seen, as the result of concussion of the eye and optic nerve produced by a blow on the forehead.

The arguments adduced from anatomy in favour of the view that the function of one nerve of sense may be performed by another, have a very weak foundation. The optic nerve of the mole was supposed to be the orbitar branch of the fifth nerve; Koch and Henle have, however, shown that the mole has a special optic nerve, uncommonly small, it is true, but corresponding in size to the eye itself; and the same may be the case in the Proteus anguinus. Treviranus and E. H. Weber have demonstrated the independence of the acoustic nerve from the fifth nerve in fishes. Even the circumstance of fibres of different function being included in one sheath, is by no means an argument for the possibility of different sensations being transmitted by one conductor. It is on the supposition of such a union of different fibres in one sheath, that we may explain the existence in fishes of a nervus accessorius nervi acoustici, which arises sometimes separately from the brain, sometimes from the fifth nerve, and sometimes from the vagus; and also the fact stated by Treviranus, that in some birds the nervus vestibuli is a branch of the facial. The olfactory nerves were supposed to be absent in the dolphin, but rudiments of them have been found by Blainville, Mayer, and Treviranus; so that it is not necessary to attribute the sense of smell in these animals to other nerves, and it is, moreover, by no means ascertained that they have any sense of smell.

Among the well-attested facts of physiology, again, there is not one to support the belief that one nerve of sense can assume the functions of another. The exaggeration of the sense of touch in the blind will not in these days be called seeing with the fingers; the accounts of the power of vision by the fingers and epigastrium, said to be possessed in the so-called magnetic state, appear to be mere fables, and the instances in which it has been pretended to practise it, cases of deception. The nerves of touch are capable of no other sensation than that of touch or feeling. Hence, also, no sounds can be heard except by the auditory nerve; the vibrations of bodies are perceived by the nerves of touch as mere tremours, a sensation wholly different in its nature from sound; though it is indeed even now not rare for the different modes of action of the vibrations of bodies upon the sense of hearing, and upon that of feeling, to be confounded. Without the organ of hearing with its vital endowments, there would be no such a thing as sound in the world, but merely vibrations; without the organ of sight, there would be no light, colour, nor darkness, but merely a corresponding presence or absence of the oscillations of the imponderable matter of light.

VII. *It is not known whether the essential cause of the peculiar "energy" of each nerve of sense is seated in the nerve itself, or in the parts of the brain and spinal cord with which it is connected; but it is certain that the central portions of the nerves included in the encephalon are susceptible of their peculiar sensations, independently of the more peripheral portion of the nervous cords which form the means of communication with the external organs of sense.*

The specific sensibility of the individual senses to particular stimuli,—owing to which vibrations of such rapidity or length as to produce sound are perceived, only by the senses of hearing and touch, and mere mechanical influences, scarcely at all by the sense of taste,—must be a property of the nerves themselves; but the peculiar mode of reaction of each sense, after the excitement of its nerve, may be due to either of two conditions. Either the nerves themselves may communicate impressions different in quality to the sensorium, which in every instance remains the same; or the vibrations of the nervous principle may in every nerve be the same and yet give rise to the perception of different sensations in the sensorium, owing to the parts of the latter with which the nerves are connected having different properties. The proof of either of these propositions I regard as at present impossible. Closely connected with this subject is the question of the existence of a difference in properties between the sensitive, motor, and organic nervous fibres. Do these fibres differ from each other by the nervous principle in each having a peculiar mode of oscillation? or are their different actions due to the parts with which they are connected as conductors? . . .

It is, however, ascertained, beyond a doubt, that certain parts of the brain participate, at least, in the peculiar energies of the senses; for pressure on the brain has been frequently observed to cause the sensation of light. Luminous spectra may still be excited by internal causes after complete amaurosis of the retina. Alex. von Humboldt states that, in a man who had lost one eye, he produced, by means of galvanism, luminous appearances on the blind side. And Luicke relates the case of a patient who, after the extirpation of the eye for fungoid disease, perceived all kinds of luminous appearances independently of external objects, and was so teased by them as to imagine he really saw them with his eyes. When he closed the remaining sound eye, he perceived different images—such as lights, circles of fire, many dancing figures, &c.—floating before the orbit whence the eye had been removed. These sensations (which are analogous to those referred to a limb lost by amputation) continued for several days.

Sometimes, also, sensations and violent pains are felt in limbs quite devoid of sensibility to external impressions. . . . It is probable that here also the central organs are the source of the sensations. Since, therefore, the peculiar energies of the senses are possessed by certain portions of the sensorium, the question really requiring solution is, Whether the nerves which are the conductors of the external impressions, participate or not in these properties or "energies." This question cannot at present be answered; for the facts that are known may be explained on either supposition. That sensations arising from internal causes are often felt in peripheral parts, cannot be regarded as an argument for the nerves possessing the special sensitive energies; since it is known that affections even of the central organs of the nervous system are often manifested in peripheral parts of the body.

VIII. *The immediate objects of the perception of our senses are merely particular states induced in the nerves, and felt as sensations either by the nerves themselves or by the sensorium; but inasmuch as the nerves of the senses are material bodies, and therefore participate in the properties of matter generally, occupying space, being susceptible of vibratory motion, and capable of being changed chemically as well as by the action of heat and electricity, they make known to the sensorium, by virtue of the changes thus produced in them by external causes, not merely their own condition, but also properties and changes of condition of external bodies. The information thus obtained by the senses concerning external nature, varies in each sense, having a relation to the qualities or energies of the nerve.*

Qualities which are to be regarded rather as sensations or modes of reaction of the nerves of sense, are light, colour, the bitter and sweet tastes, pleasant and unpleasant odours, painful and pleasant impressions on the nerves of touch, cold and warmth: properties which may belong wholly to external nature are "extension," progressive and tremulous motion, and chemical change.

All the senses are not equally adapted to impart the idea of "extension" to the sensorium. The nerve of vision and the nerve of touch, being capable of an exact perception of this property in themselves, make us acquainted with it in external bodies. In the nerves of taste, the sensation of extension is less distinct, but is not altogether deficient; thus we are capable of distinguishing whether the seat of a bitter or sweet taste be the tongue, the palate, or the fauces. In the sense of touch and sight, however, the perception of space is most acute. The retina of the optic nerve has a structure especially adapted for this perception; for the ends of the nervous fibres in the retina are, as Treviranus discovered, so arranged as to be at last perpendicular to its inner surface, and by their papillar extremities form a pavement-like composite membrane. On the great number of these terminal fibrils depends the delicate power of discriminating the position of bodies in space possessed by the sense of vision; for each fibre represents a greater or less field of the visible world, and imparts the impression of it to the sensorium.

The sense of touch has a much more extended sphere of action for the perception of space than has the sense of vision; but its perception of this quality of external bodies is much less accurate, and considerable portions of the surface of the body or skin are in many instances represented in the sensorium by very few nervous fibres; hence, in many parts of the surface, impressions on two points considerably removed from each other are, as E. H. Weber has shown, felt as one impression. Although the senses of vision, touch, and taste are all capable of perceiving the property of extension in space, yet the quality of the sensations which give the conception of extension is different in each of these senses; the sensation in one is an image of which the essential quality is light; in another, a perception of extension with any of the modifications of the quality of touch, between pain, cold, heat, and pleasure; in the third, a perception of extension with the quality of taste.

The external cause which excites in the organ of sense the sensation which conveys also the notion of extension, may be various. In the organ of vision it is usually the external light, but a concussion given to the eye by an external body may also be the cause; for example, if a determinate portion of the retina is pressed upon, a luminous spectrum is produced at that part, which will occupy a definite portion of the field of vision. Even electricity applied to the eyes can give rise to images of definite extent and form, such as lines of fire, the position of which varies according to the position of the poles of the galvanic battery: to the consideration of these phenomena we shall return. Light also may excite in the organ of touch a sensation with definite extent; for instance, the sensation of the parts warmed by the light of the sun has its limits as to extent. But ordinarily the impressions which inform us of the qualities and conditions of external bodies through the medium of the sense of touch, are mechanical contact, friction, concussion, pressure, or the communication of the vibrations of bodies, which we feel as tremours. By means of mechanical impressions on the sense of touch we obtain the first and most important information regarding the form and density of bodies, of which information reason afterwards makes use to interpret the perceptions of the other senses.

The distribution of nerves of common sensation throughout the entire mass of the limbs, indeed throughout most parts of our body, gives to our sense of touch the faculty of distinguishing the extension of our own body in all its dimensions; for each point in which a nervous fibre terminates is represented in the sensorium.

Collision with other bodies also, if forcible enough, may excite
sensation to a certain depth in the mass of our body, and produce
the perception of contusion in all the dimensions of the "cube."
Usually, however, the three senses which make us acquainted with
the space occupied by bodies, submit to our perception the property of superficial extension only, owing to the exciting causes acting only on the sentient surfaces. The sense of touch has, however,
here this advantage over the sense of vision, that the parts endowed with it can be made to embrace a body in several directions; and although the sensation even then affords essentially
only a perception of superficial extension, namely, of that of the
surface of our body corresponding to the surfaces of the object,
yet the mind, by taking into account the movements required for
the embrace of the object, obtains from a sensation of superficial
extent an idea of a body with a certain cubic capacity.

There exists in this respect less real difference between the
sense of vision and that of touch than is generally supposed. To
place them on an equality, it is only requisite that the eye should
be able to change its position so as to look towards the different
surfaces of an object; and this defect can be supplied by changing
the relative position of our body and the object.

The sense of hearing is almost totally incapable of perceiving
the quality of extension; and for this reason, that the organ of
hearing has no perception of its own extension. The cause of this
difference between the senses is not known. The retina, even when
the subject of no excitement from without, perceives its own extension and locality as darkness before the eyes. The organ of
smell is sensible at least of the organ in which the odours are perceived, and is conscious of the whole cavity of the nostrils being
occupied by a penetrating odour; we cannot make the odorous
substance act on less than the entire nasal cavity. With respect to
the sense of hearing, on the contrary, we have no perception at
all of the part at which the sound is heard.

The sensation of motion is, like motion itself, of two kinds,—
progressive and vibratory. The faculty of the perception of progressive motion is enjoyed in different manners by the three senses
of vision, touch, and taste,—by those senses, therefore, which are
capable of recognising extension in space generally, on which

capability the former faculty is indeed dependent, and of which it is the mere result. An impression is perceived travelling from one part of the retina to another, and the movement of the image is interpreted by the imagination as motion of the object; the same is the case in the sense of touch. The movement of a sensation of taste over the surface of the organ of taste can also be recognised.

The motion of tremors, or vibrations, is perceived by several senses. This faculty is most evident in the cases of hearing and touch; but even the retina and optic nerve appear to be capable of distinguishing such impressions. In the first place, with regard to the sense of hearing, it is known that vibrations communicated through the conducting apparatus of the ear, and lastly through the fluid of the labyrinth to the auditory nerve, are, if rapid, perceived merely as a continuous tone, the acuteness of which varies with the rapidity of succession of the vibrations; but, if they succeed each other slowly, the auditory nerve becomes to a certain degree sensible of the successive vibrations as an intermittent sound, and not merely of the general impression as a continued tone.

The vibrations which in the organ of hearing give rise to the sensation of sound, are perceived by nerves of touch in the skin as tremors frequently attended with the general impression of tickling; for instance, when a vibrating body, such as a tuning fork, is approximated to a very sensible part of the surface. These are completely parallel phenomena to those produced by vibrations in the organ of hearing. Just as the latter organ perceives the impulses of a vibrating body separately as a series of unmusical sounds, and their rapid succession as a continuous tone, so the nerve of touch is sensible of distinct tremors, and if the vibrations succeed each other with sufficient rapidity, becomes the seat of the itching or tickling sensation peculiar to the sense of touch.

The experiments of Savart with the toothed wheel, and those of Cagniard la Tour with the siren, . . . have proved that the undulatory motion of vibrations is not necessary for the production of the sensation of sound in the organ of hearing, and that a rapid succession of mere impulses has the same effect, producing a musical note. In this respect, also, the action of the impulses of a body upon the nerves of touch forms a parallel to the phenomena produced in the organ of hearing; for the nerves of touch, brought into contact with a vibrating tuning-fork, receives a succession of impulses, of which each singly would not produce the sensation of tickling or itching.

The faculty of discerning the rate of succession of impressions is possessed by all the senses, though in a high degree only by the auditory nerves, in which its delicacy is very remarkable.

The instrument invented by M. Savart, in which tones are produced by the friction of the teeth of a revolving wheel against a hard body, has afforded the means of determining more accurately than was before possible the deepest and most acute notes perceptible by the ear. Savart has shown that tones which correspond to 24,000 impulses, or 48,000 simple vibrations, in a second, if of proper intensity, may still be heard. Two impulses succeeding each other, or four successive vibrations, are sufficient to form a tone of which the pitch can be compared with that of other tones; that is to say, a tone which, if continued a second, would require 1000 impulses to produce it, will be recognisable if only two of the impulses are heard, and will be distinguishable from another sound which in a second would have 2000, or more or less impulses. From this it results that the sense of hearing can discriminate the interval of $\frac{1}{12000}$ of a second, since 24,000 impulses in a second upon Savart's instrument produced the most acute sound which could be perceived by the ear.

The eye can communicate to the sensorium the image of a vibrating body, and can distinguish the vibrations when they are very slow; but here the vibrations are not communicated to the optic nerve in such a manner that the latter repeats them, or that it receives their impulses; while in the ear the vibrations can be imparted directly to the auditory nerve, in consequence of this nerve being spread out on parts which contain the "fluid of the labyrinth." The optic nerve is not in the condition either to propagate or to receive vibrations, such as those of a sonorous body; to adapt it for such a purpose, it would require to be spread out, like the auditory nerves, upon sac-like membranes, filled and surrounded externally with fluid, and to have connected with it an apparatus for conducting the vibrations from without. If the optic nerve were, like the nerves of hearing and touch, capable of the perception of vibrations, the effect of the propagation of the vibration of an external body through the air to the retina would be a general appearance of light, just as sound is the result in the auditory nerve. I have already mentioned that the impulses of a vibrating tuning-fork brought into contact with the eye, are not adequate to excite the peculiar sensibility of the optic nerve. The cause of this may be either that the impulses are too feeble, or that they succeed each other too slowly. The feebleness of the impulses which do not strike immediately upon the retina, is probably a principal cause; for a stronger impulse upon those parts of the eye where the retina exists, produces the sensation of light. It is possible, also, that very feeble impulses, if repeated with much greater rapidity, and acting on the retina itself, would excite its peculiar sensation—light. Such is the mode of action of external light upon the eye according to the "undulation theory," which has gained increased probability during the later steps of the science of physics. Newton applied the theory of the undulations of light to the explanation of vision. According to the "undulatory theory," colours are the result of the different rapidity of the vibration and length of the undulations. The undulations which excite in the eye the sensation of violet, are the shortest; according to Herschell's calculation, their length is 0.0000167 of an inch, and their number in a second is 727,000000,000000. The undulations of the red ray are the longest; their length being 0.0000266, and their number in a second 458,000000,000000. The vibrations of bodies which excite the sensation of sound in our sense of hearing are much slower. The column of air of the thirty-two feet organ-pipe vibrates thirty-two times in a second; and, according to M. Savart, tones are perceptible which result from seven or eight impulses only during a second, each impulse having a duration of $\frac{1}{16}$ of a second.

We are made acquainted with chemical actions by several senses, but principally by taste, smell, and touch, and by each of these senses in the mode proper to it. Volatile bodies disturbing the conditions of the nerves by a chemical action, exert the greatest influence upon the organ of smell; and many matters act on that sense which produce no impression upon the organs of taste and touch,—for example, many odorous substances, as the vapours of metals, of lead for instance, and of many minerals, &c.

It cannot, however, be stated as a general rule that volatile substances are perceived only by the sense of smell; for the same substances are also capable of impressing the senses of touch and taste, provided they are of a nature adapted to disturb chemically the condition of those organs, and in the case of the organ of taste are dissolved by the fluids covering it. Some volatile substances— as, the vapours of horse-radish and mustard, and acrid suffocating gases,—act very powerfully upon the common sensitive nerves of certain tracts of mucous membrane, as the conjunctiva and the mucous membrane of the lungs, exciting merely modifications of common feeling; many volatile matters also excite the sensations of burning, pain, &c. in the organ of touch when the skin is denuded of its epidermis.

It is not known whether fluid bodies are capable of exciting the peculiar energy of the organ of smell [in man]; and, owing to the position of the organ, we have little opportunity of deciding the question by experiment. Although nothing of the kind has ever hitherto been observed in man, it is not à priori to be regarded as impossible, since even volatile substances must be dissolved by the fluids of the mucous surface of the organ of smell before they can act on the olfactory nerves. Fishes, however, afford us a direct example of smell being excited by substances in the fluid state; and I cannot conceive why the nerves of smell in any animal should not be excited to their peculiar sensation by a fluid which excites in the nerves of taste the sensation of taste. The perception of odours in the air and water bear the same relation to each other as respiration in the air and water.

Fluid bodies, applied to the organs of touch and taste, produce chemical disturbances in their nerves, which excite in each a different sensation; mustard, alkalies, acids, and salts, produce upon the skin, and upon the tongue, the totally different effects. Their chemical action must primarily be the same; but the reaction excited differs according to the property of the nerves. On the tongue, however, both results are most probably produced in different nervous fibres at the same time, and by the same substance. Of all the nerves of sense, that of taste is most exposed to chemical influences, and is most affected by very slight modifications of the chemical constitution of bodies. The different conditions as to sensation, into which the nerves of touch can be thrown by chemical agents, are not by any means so numerous; moreover, these nerves are, at least upon the skin, (not on the mucous membranes,) protected from chemical influences by the epidermis.

In consequence of their contact with and action against external chemical influences, the three senses, smell, taste, and touch, become important instruments for the distinction and recognition of different substances, although neither of them reveals to us anything of their internal properties. The impressions produced on the senses by bodies similarly constituted are not always the same, and those produced by bodies of different chemical constitution are not constantly different.

The senses of sight and hearing are not exposed to the action of chemical influences from without; but it must not thence be concluded that they are insusceptible of excitement by such influences.

An important difference between the senses has reference to the proximity or distance of the bodies concerning which they give us information. Strictly speaking, the senses make us conscious only of that which is immediately present in them. By the eye we do not really perceive the luminous body; but the ends of the rays emitted from it strike the retina, and the parts of that membrane thus acted on become the seat of sensation. By the ear we do not feel the vibrating body, but merely the impulses transmitted to it from that body. Our imagination influences and modifies so powerfully the idea communicated to our sensorium by the act of vision, that this sense appears to us to have an action exterior to our body, and, in place of the images depicted on the surface of the retina, the imagination conceives the idea of real objects; the image of a country, which occupies the space of a window, seems to the imagination an immediate perception of the different near and distant objects. In the senses of smell, taste, and touch, the imagination cannot have so great an influence: we refer, it is true, the sensations in the nerves to the objects themselves; but, since the objects excite the sensations of taste and touch by immediate contact, we become on reflection immediately conscious that our notions concerning the properties of the bodies are derived with only a relative degree of certainty from the affections which they induce in our organs of sense.

IX. *That sensations are referred from their proper seat towards the exterior, is owing, not to anything in the nature of the nerves themselves, but to the accompanying idea derived from experience.*

To know the first independent action of our senses distinct from the results of their education, it would be necessary that we had a full recollection of the first impressions made upon them independently of the ideas obtained through their means. This is impossible. Obscure ideas arise even from the first impressions on the senses of the child. It only remains for us then to analyse the act of sensation and the idea with reference to their real import. Doing this, we find in the act of the mind which accompanies sensation, opposed to each other, *the percipient conscious subject,* or self, of the sentient body whose conditions, whether internal or determined from without, are objects for this "conscious self," and the *external world,* with which the sentient body is brought into collision. To the mental consciousness,—to the "self" of the animal being,—every sensation, every motive from without, every "passion" in the logical sense, is something external. The "self" of the individual opposes itself as a free "subject" to the most intense sensations,—to the most tormenting pains. The limb which gives us pain can be removed without the integrity of the individual spirit being diminished; the "self" of the being may be deprived of most of the limbs (parts) of the organic body, and yet be itself as perfect as before; but we have thus far made no distinction between the "exterior" which the organised limbs of our body form in relation to the consciousness of our "self," and the "exterior" which the external world itself forms with regard to our body. The origin of this distinction can be recognised most easily in the sense of touch, which is the first to come into collision with the external world. If we imagine a human being, in which—as in the foetus in utero, for example,—the sense of vision has never received any impressions, and in which sensations of touch merely have been excited by impressions made upon its body from without, it is evident that the first obscure idea excited could be no other than that of a sentient passive "self" in contradistinction to something acting upon it. The uterus, which compels the child to assume a determined position, and gives rise to sensations in it, is also the means of exciting in the sensorium of the child the consciousness of something thus distinct from itself and external to it. But how is the idea of two "exteriors,"—of that which the limbs of the child's body forms in relation to its internal self, and of the true exterior world,—developed? In a twofold manner. In the first place, the child governs the movements of its limbs, and thus perceives that they are instruments subject to the use and government of its internal "self;" while the resistance which it meets with around is not subject to its will, and therefore gives it the idea of an absolute exterior. Secondly, the child will perceive a difference in the sensations produced, according as two parts of its own body touch each other, or as one part of its body only meets with resistance from without. In the first instance, where one arm, for example, touches the other, the resistance is afforded by a part of the child's own body, and the limb thus giving the resistance becomes the subject of sensation as well as the other. The two limbs are in this case external objects of perception, and percipient at the same time. In the second instance, the resisting body will be represented to the mind as something external and foreign to the living body, and not subject to the internal "self." Thus will arise in the mind of the child the idea of a resistance which one part of its own body can offer to other parts of its body, and at the same time the idea of a resistance offered to its body by an absolute "exterior." In this way is gained the idea of an external world as the cause of sensations. Though the sensations of the being actually inform him only of the states of himself, of his nerves, and of his skin, acted on by external impressions, yet, henceforth, the idea of the perception of the external cause becomes inseparably associated with the sensation of touch; and such the condition of sensation in the adult. If we lay our hand upon a table, we become conscious, on a little reflection, that we do not feel the table, but merely that part of our skin which the table touches; but, without this reflection, we confound the sensation of the part of the skin which has received the impression with the idea of the resistance, and we maintain boldly that we feel the table itself, which is not the case. If the hand be now moved over a greater extent of the table's surface, the idea of a larger object than the hand can cover is obtained. If, to encompass the resisting object, the hand require to be moved in different directions and planes, the idea of surfaces applied to each other in different directions is conceived, and thus the notion of an external solid body occupying space obtained.

Our perception by sensation of the muscular movements necessary for thus passing our hand over the different surfaces of an object, is the immediate source of our idea of the external body; for the first idea of a body having extension and occupying space arises in our mind from the sensation of our own corporeal extension. This consciousness of our own corporeal existence is the standard by which we estimate in our sense of touch the extension of all resisting bodies. The question, whether the idea of space is originally innate in our sensorium, and influences all our perceptions, or whether it is the result of experience, may be here passed over: we shall return to it in discussing the physiology of the mental faculties. Thus much only is certain, that even though the idea of space did not originally exist as an obscure faculty in the sensorium, which is afterwards called into action and applied when sensations begin to be perceived, it would assuredly be obtained by experience in the first acts of the sense of touch.

The obscure conceptions of a percipient body opposed to the external world, and itself occupying space, concerning the attribute of extension, or corporeal existence of external things, already exist, therefore, and have acquired some degree of lucidity and certainty before birth, at which time the sense of vision comes into action. The sensations of vision, in consequence of this, become soon intelligible; and the ideas already obtained through the means of the sense of touch are readily applied to their interpretation.

It is exceedingly difficult, if not quite impossible, to form a conception in any degree probable of the mode in which the child judges of the first impressions made upon the retina, and to decide whether it regards the image in its eye as a part of its own body, or as something external. The image cannot at all events be regarded as identical with the percipient "subject," or "self;" for, like pain and everything that is felt, it is an object opposed to this "self" of the child; but whether, as an object, it be looked upon as a part of the living body, or as something external and removed from it, is not so easily decided. It has been frequently asserted to be a peculiar property of the sense of vision that the sensation perceived by it does not, as in the sense of touch, appear to occupy the seat of its production,—that the retina does not perceive any sensations in itself; and that the sensation becomes an object of perception, not in the retina, but far distant from it. This cannot, however, be asserted thus absolutely; for the appearance of darkness before the eyes when closed, which is the sensation of the repose and unexcited state of the retina, seems to us to exist only in front of the eyes,—that is, in the situation of the sentient organ,—and neither behind us, nor at the sides, nor in the distance. And this dark field of vision of the closed eyes is the same frame, the same *tabula rasa,* in which, when the eyes are opened, all the images of visible forms appear as the results of the affection of determinate parts of the retina.

If the ideas of external objects, as the causes of sensation, had not already been gained by means of the sense of touch, the first use of the sense of vision would be attended with the same process as we have described to accompany the first acts of touch. The affections of the retina would be objects to the "conscious self" of the child; but whether they belonged to the living body, or were external to it, would not be evident. The child is, however, born already furnished with obscure ideas of objects external to its own body,—with ideas of their real existence as causes of sensations; and sensation and the idea of the external object of perception are already confounded in its sensorium. The next steps of the process, as far as they can be imagined with probability, will be these:

The images of objects are formed in the retina in one surface, just as the retina is extended in that form. They will appear to the mind as depicted on a surface, and will excite no idea of proximity or distance, or of the actual occupation of space. However soon the child may recognise the images as things exterior to itself, they still appear to it to occupy one plane, to be all at the same distance from it: it catches at the most distant, as at the nearest object,—it grasps at the moon. The boy born blind, to whom Cheselden restored sight by operation, saw all objects as if they lay in one plane, although in him the ideas of the corporeal world obtained through the sense of touch were completely developed. It seemed to him as if the objects "touched his eyes as what he felt did his skin."

The images of external bodies will be distinguished from the image of one's own body, which presents itself with them in the field of vision in the following manner. A part of our body throws an image, like external bodies, upon our retina. The part of our body thus visible with external objects, varies in size according to our position; it may be a large or a small portion of the trunk, or of the limbs: the part of the head of which an image can be formed in the retina is very small, such as the sides or tip of the nose, the eyebrows when depressed, and sometimes also the lips. This image of our own body occupies, in nearly all pictures on our retina, regularly some determinate space in the upper, middle, or lower part of the field of vision; it remains constant while the other images are continually changing.

The image of its own body being constant in its position, will in this way be soon distinguished by the child from those images which change their place when the body or eyes of the child are moved. From the movements, also, of this image of a part of its own body, the child will soon still more certainly conceive the idea of its possessing a body distinct from the absolutely external bodies; for these movements of the image in the retina will be observed to correspond to real movements of its body determined by the will. With the visual perceptions of its body will become connected perceptions of touch. The child, touching another part of its body with its hand, will see this act performed by the image in the retina; the image of its hand will touch the image of the other part of its body. In this way certain ideas become so inseparably connected with the sensations of vision, that not only does the image, which consists essentially merely in an affection of aliquot parts of our retina, seem to be external to, and removed to a distance from us, but the sensations come to be regarded as perfectly identical with the objects themselves, notwithstanding their difference of size.

Even the superficial expansion of the field of vision is soon converted by the imagination into a space extending in all directions; for, with every movement of our body, with every step forwards, the forms of the images undergo a change, the remote become near, and the near objects present other surfaces to our view. This change in the images depicted on our retina during the locomotion of our body, must convey to the mind the idea of our moving in space between the different images,—of our advancing through the midst of them; for, during this locomotion, the image of our own body in the field of vision becomes constantly associated with new images of external objects, and the locomotion is the cause of this displacement of the images.

From the foregoing considerations, we conclude that it is owing to the combined action of the mind and the nerves, and not to the action of the sense alone, which would merely perceive the changes produced in itself, that the sensation really seated in the nerve seems to us to be something exterior to the body.

X. *The mind not only perceives the sensations and interprets them according to ideas previously obtained, but it has a direct influence upon them, imparting to them intensity. This influence of the mind, in the case of the senses which have the power of distinguishing the property of extension in objects, may be confined to definite parts of the sentient organ; in the sense gifted with the power of distinguishing with delicacy intervals of time, it may be confined to particular acts of sensation. It also has the power of giving to one sense a predominant activity.*

The attention cannot be directed to many impressions at the same time: in proportion as coetaneous impressions on the senses become numerous, the sensations diminish in intensity, or the mind receives one only with distinctness; while the others are only obscurely, or not at all perceived. If the attention be withdrawn from the nerves of sense, and engaged in intellectual contemplation, deep speculations, or an intense passion, the sensations of the nerves make no impression upon the mind; they are not perceived,—that is to say, they are not communicated to the conscious "self," or with so little intensity, that the mind is at the moment, on account of being quite preoccupied by some other idea, unable to retain the impression, or only recollects it some time after, when the equilibrium of the sensorium is restored, and it is freed from the preponderating influence of the idea which had occupied it. The acuteness which individual senses acquire when others are quite inactive, is therefore readily intelligible; the attention is no longer divided between the several senses, but is wholly engaged in the analysis of the sensations of one.

The blind man acquires such an extraordinary acuteness of touch, as to distinguish with facility the minute elevations on the surface of money, for example; sometimes, indeed, he is able to discriminate between the corpus or grain of one colouring matter and that of another.

By an effort of the mind, however, the detail of a single sensation may be analysed. Since the mind is not capable of directing an equally accurate attention to every part of the cutaneous surface excited to sensation, an acute perception of the state of every part can be attained only by the mind being rapidly directed from the nervous fibres of one part to those of another. By this influence of the mind, an extraordinary degree of troublesome acuteness and permanence may be given to a slight itching sensation at any point of the skin of the face, while it ceases spontaneously when forgotten. The same influence of the mind is evinced in the sense of vision. If we endeavoured to direct our attention to the whole field of vision at the same time, we should see nothing distinctly, but our mental activity is directed first to this, then to that part, and analyses the detail of the sensation, the part to which the mind is directed being perceived with more distinctness than the rest of the same sensation. This does not arise from the middle of the retina, at which the sensibility is greatest, being turned towards the different parts of the object in succession; for, while the position of the axes of the eyes remains the same, we can by a mental effort render the perception of side objects more vivid than they were previously. Without changing the direction of the axis of vision, we can observe in succession the separate elements of a compound mathematical figure, which we are regarding, more accurately than the rest of the figure, which for the time we disregard. A polygonal figure, divided in its interior into different parts by lines, produces a different impression according as the attention is directed to this or that part of the whole: a single triangle in the figure may wholly occupy our attention; at the next moment the attention may be transferred to another figure intersecting the triangle, which, though it existed before, was not observed while the mind was directed to the triangle. The same process takes place in examining architectural ornaments, as roses and arabesques; and the charm which these figures possess, consists in great part in their exciting a vivid action of the attention on different parts of the objects so as to cause them even to present to us an appearance of life. We ordinarily see with both eyes simultaneously when their power of vision is equal; but the mental influence is able to render predominant in intensity the visual impression of one eye, as we shall hereafter prove by experiment; and it may be distinctly demonstrated that, in seeing with both eyes, although under ordinary circumstances we are unconscious of it, a striving for predominance of the sensation takes place between them, and that the sensation perceived is quite different according to the relative intensity of their actions. The experiment of looking upon a sheet of white paper through two differently coloured glasses at the same time, may serve as an illustration for the present. The impressions of blue and yellow, for example, are found in such an experiment not to mingle readily; at one moment the blue, at another the yellow is predominant. Sometimes blue nebulous spots are seen upon the yellow field; at other times, yellow spots of varying magnitude upon the blue field: sometimes one colour alone prevails, and has absorbed the other; sometimes the reverse is seen. The appearance of one colour in spots upon a ground of the other colour, shows indeed that the attention can be directed at the same time to one part of one retina, and to other parts of the other retina.

The influence of mental action upon the sense of hearing, which is not, like the senses of sight and touch, capable of the perception of corporeal extension in space, but has the most vivid perception of the succession of intervals of time in relation to impressions, is of another kind. The discriminating power of the organ of hearing, as to place, amounts at the most to the capability of determining whether the sound be heard with the one or the other ear, or by which it is heard most acutely; and then, when different words are addressed to the respective ears, the attention may be directed more to one impression than to the other. The influence of the attention, however, in distinguishing feeble sounds is highly remarkable: usually we do not perceive the more feeble tones of strings and other musical instruments; but, by attention, we cause their impression, as well as that of the slightest noise, upon the sensorium to become vivid. Still more remarkable is the faculty we possess of distinguishing by attention each of the many tones simultaneously emitted by an orchestra, and even of following the weaker tones of one instrument apart from the other sounds, of which the impressions are then less vividly perceived.

In concluding this introduction to the physiology of the senses, the question naturally presents itself: Is the number of the senses limited? may not some animals be endowed with other senses besides those which we possess? The error into which Spallanzani fell, in ascribing a peculiar sense to bats on account of their expertness of flight along the surface of walls when they could not see them, is well known. Many persons again have ascribed to animals a peculiar sense by reason of their foreknowledge of the changes of weather. Since the state of the atmospheric pressure, the quantity of watery vapour in the atmosphere, temperature, and electricity, have so marked an influence on the animal economy of our own bodies, that we are sensible of changes which they undergo, the possibility of such and even greater influences on animals may very well be conceived, but even great dependence on the state of the atmosphere with reference to sensation does not require a new sense. On the contrary, the state of the atmosphere may be perceived by its influence on the whole nervous system, and particularly through the sensations of the nerves which are most numerous, and most exposed to the atmosphere, namely, the nerves of touch or common sensation. The supposed existence of a special sense for the perception of electricity in some animals is, *à priori*, not admissible; for electricity acts, as we have already shown, upon all the senses, exciting in each the sensations peculiar to it.

The essential attribute of a new sense is, not the perception of external objects or influences which ordinarily do not act upon the senses, but that external causes should excite in it a new and peculiar kind of sensation different from all the sensations of our five senses. Such peculiar kind of sensation will depend on the powers of the nervous system; and the possibility of the possession of such a faculty by some animals cannot, à priori, be denied: no facts, however, are known which establish the existence of such a new mode of sensation, and it is, in fact, quite impossible to have any experience of the nature of a sensation in any other beings than ourselves.

Some physiologists have regarded the internal sensations of the sense of touch by which we are made acquainted with the different states of our body, as something different from that sense, and have ranked the conscious perception of the different parts of our frame (Gemeingefühl, coenaesthesis, or common feeling,) almost on a level with the other senses. This is an error; for the sensations here alluded to are of the same nature as those of the skin which are excited from without, only that in many organs they are more undefined and obscure. Moreover, it is indifferent whether a sense be excited to action from within, or from without; in no sense do we perceive any essential difference between the sensations thus produced. The designation, "sense of touch," expresses certainly a special relation of that sense to the external world; but the act of "touch" merely renders manifest the energies of this sense, which everywhere resides in the same nerves—the mixed cerebral and spinal nerves with double roots. Something analogous to the act of touch is observed in the other senses; it is an action of the sense voluntarily directed; and in the same way there is a voluntary hearing (listening), seeing (looking), tasting, and smelling.

*   *   *

The final passage in this chapter presents the essence of Helmholtz's three-element theory of color vision. This theory can be viewed as an attempt, analogous to that of Müller and following

the lead of Bell and Magendie, to uncover the physico-physiological basis for qualitative differences in sensory experience
within a single modality. What are the mechanisms that make it
possible for us to experience the many colors in the visible spectrum? The answer given by Helmholtz in the following excerpt
is one that has enjoyed only minimal opposition, and, the recent
highly controversial ideas of Land* aside, it remains the dominant
theory of color vision even today, a century after it was first
proposed.

Hermann Ludwig von Helmholtz

The Compound Colors

. . . Every difference of impression made by light, as we have
seen, may be regarded as a function of three independent variables; and the three variables which have been chosen thus far
were (1) the luminosity, (2) the hue, and (3) the saturation, or
(1) the quantity of white, (2) the quantity of some colour of
the spectrum, and (3) the wave-length of this colour. However,
instead of these variables, three others may also be employed;
and in fact this is what it amounts to, when all colours are regarded as being mixtures of variable amounts of *three so-called
fundamental colours,* which are generally taken to be *red, yellow*
and *blue.* To conceive this theory objectively, and to assert that
there are simple colours in the spectrum which can be combined
to produce a visual impression that will be the same as that pro-

H. v. Helmholtz. *Helmholtz's treatise on physiological optics.* Translated from the
3rd German edition (1909–1911) by several hands. Edited by J. P. C. Southall.
Rochester, N. Y.: Optical Society of America, 1924–1925. The first German edition
of *Handbuch der physiologischen optik* was published between 1856 and 1866.
This selection is from Vol. II, pp. 141–145 of the Southall translation.

* E. H. Land. Experiments in color vision. *Scientific American,* 1959, **5,**
84–99.

duced by any other simple or compound light, would not be correct. There are no such three simple colours that can be combined to match the other colours of the spectrum even fairly well, because the colours of the spectrum invariably appear to be more saturated than the composite colours. Least suited for this purpose are red, yellow and blue; for if we take for blue a colour like the hue of the sky, and not a more greenish blue, it will be impossible to get green at all by mixing these colours. By taking a greenish yellow and a greenish blue, the best we can get is a very pale green. These three colours would not have been selected, had it not been that most persons, relying on the mixture of pigments, made the mistake of thinking that a mixture of yellow and blue light gives green. It would be rather better to take *violet, green* and *red* for fundamental colours. Blue can be obtained by mixing violet and green, but it is not the saturated blue of the spectrum; and a dead yellow can be made with green and red, which is not at all like the brilliant yellow in the spectrum.

If we think of the colours as plotted on a colour-chart by the method sketched [Figure 1], it is evident from the rules given for the construction that all colours that are to be made by mixing three colours must be contained within the triangle whose vertices are the places in the chart where the three fundamental colours are. Thus, in the adjoining colour circle, where the positions of the colours are indicated by the initial letters of their names

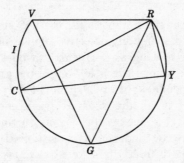

Figure 1

(I = indigo-blue, C = cyan-blue, Y = yellow, G = green, etc.), all the colours that can be made by mixing red, cyan-blue and yellow are comprised within the triangle RCY. Thus, as we see, two large pieces of the circle are missing, and all that could be obtained would be a very pale violet and a very pale green. But if, instead of cyan-blue, the colour of the blue sky, indigo-blue, were taken, green would be missing entirely. The triangle VRG comprises the colours obtained by mixing violet, red and green, and a larger number of the existing colours would indeed be represented. But, as the diagram shows, large portions of the circle are still missing, as must always be the case according to the results of experiments on the mixture of the colours of the spectrum. The conclusion is that the boundary of the colour chart must be a curved line which differs considerably from the perimeter of the triangle.

Brewster, endeavouring to defend the objective nature of three fundamental colours, maintained that for every wave-length there were three different kinds of light, red, yellow and blue, mixed merely in different proportions so as to give the different colours of the spectrum. Thus, the colours of the spectrum were considered as being compound colours consisting of three kinds of light of different quality; although the degree of refrangibility of the rays was the same for each individual simple colour. Brewster's idea was that light of all three fundamental colours could be proved to exist in the different simple colours by the absorption of light by coloured media. His entire theory is based on this conception, which was shown in the preceding chapter to be erroneous.

Apart from Brewster's hypothesis, the notion of three fundamental colours as having any objective significance has no meaning anyhow. For as long as it is simply a question of physical relations, and the human eye is left out of the game, the properties of the compound light are dependent only on the relative amounts of light of all the separate wave-lengths it contains. When we speak of reducing the colours to three fundamental colours, this must be understood in a subjective sense and as being an attempt to trace the *colour sensations* to three *fundamental sensations*. This was the way that Young regarded the problem; and, in fact, his theory affords an exceedingly simple and clear explanation of all the phenomena of the physiological colour theory. He supposes that:

1. The eye is provided with three distinct sets of nervous fibres. Stimulation of the first excites the sensation of red, stimulation of the second the sensation of green, and stimulation of the third the sensation of violet.

2. Objective homogeneous light excites these three kinds of fibres in various degrees, depending on its wave-length. The red-sensitive fibres are stimulated most by light of longest wave-length, and the violet-sensitive fibres by light of shortest wave-length. But this does not mean that each colour of the spectrum does not stimulate all three kinds of fibres, some feebly and others strongly; on the contrary, in order to explain a series of phenomena, it is necessary to assume that that is exactly what does happen. Suppose that the colours of the spectrum are plotted horizontally [as in the accompanying figure] in their natural sequence, from red to violet, the three curves may be taken to indicate something like the degree of excitation of the three kinds of fibres, No. 1 for the red-sensitive fibres, No. 2 for the green-sensitive fibres, and No. 3 for the violet-sensitive fibres.

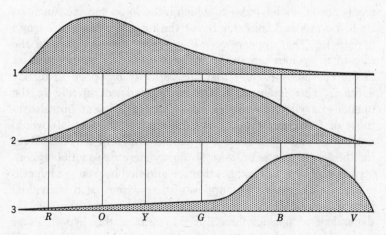

Figure 2

Pure *red* light stimulates the red-sensitive fibres strongly and the two other kinds of fibres feebly; giving the sensation red.

Pure *yellow* light stimulates the red-sensitive and green-sensitive fibres moderately and the violet-sensitive fibres feebly; giving the sensation yellow.

Pure *green* light stimulates the green-sensitive fibres strongly, and the two other kinds much more feebly; giving the sensation green.

Pure *blue* light stimulates the green-sensitive and violet-sensitive fibres moderately, and the red-sensitive fibres feebly; giving the sensation blue.

Pure *violet* light stimulates the violet-sensitive fibres strongly, and the other fibres feebly; giving the sensation violet.

When all the fibres are stimulated about equally, the sensation is that of *white* or pale hues.

It might be natural to suppose that on this hypothesis the number of nervous fibres and nerve-endings would have to be trebled, as compared with the number ordinarily assumed when each single fibre is made to conduct all possible colour stimulations. However, in the writer's opinion there is nothing in Young's hypothesis that is opposed to the anatomical facts in this respect; because we are entirely ignorant as to the number of conducting fibres, and there are also quantities of other microscopical elements (cells, nuclei, rods) to which hitherto no specific functions could be ascribed. But this is not the essential thing in Young's hypothesis. That appears to the writer to consist rather in the idea of the colour sensations being composed of three processes in the nervous substance that are perfectly independent of one another. This independence is manifested not merely in the phenomena which are being considered at present but also in those of fatigue of the nervous mechanism of vision. It would not be absolutely necessary to assume different nervous fibres for these different sensations. So far as mere explanation is concerned, the same advantages that are afforded by Young's hypothesis could be gained by supposing that within each individual fibre there might occur three activities all different from and independent of one another. But the form of this hypothesis as originally proposed by Young is clearer in both conception and expression than it would be if it were modified as suggested, and hence it will be retained in its original concrete form, for the sake of exposition if for nothing else. Nowhere in the physical (electrical) phenomena of nervous stimulation either in the sensory or motor nerves can there be detected any such differentiation of activity as must exist if each fibre of the optic nerve has to transmit all the colour sensations. By Young's hypothesis it is possible even in this connection to transfer directly to the optic nerve the simple conceptions as to the mechanism of the stimulation and its conduction which we were led to form at first by studying the phenomena in the motor nerves. This would not be the case on the assumption that each fibre of the optic nerve has to sustain three different kinds of states of stimulation which do not mutually interfere with one another. Young's hypothesis is only a more special application of the law of specific sense energies. Just as tactile sensation and visual sensation in the eye are demonstrably affairs of different nervous fibres, the same thing is assumed here too with respect to the various sensations of the fundamental colours. . . .

*   *   *

It should be noted in passing that Helmholtz created an auditory theory similar in form to his theory of color vision. Here, the main problem was to account for qualitative differences in tonal experience, and the solution again was to postulate separate receptors, linearly spread over the basilar membrane of the inner ear, each receptor being especially sensitive to a small band of sound wave frequencies by virtue of its location in a resonating system. And again, despite some quite apparent deficiencies,* the theory has had no serious rivals in the century of its existence, except perhaps that of Wever and Bray,† who have incorporated Helmholtz's theory into a more complex one of their own.

* See G. von Békésy and W. A. Rosenblith. The mechanical properties of the ear, in S. S. Stevens (ed.), *Handbook of experimental psycholgy.* New York: Wiley, 1951.
† E. G. Wever. *Theory of hearing.* New York: Wiley, 1949.

3

Illusions and Other Curiosities

It is not easy for the uninitiated to recognize the existence of a "problem of perception" in those cases where perception and "physical reality" are in close agreement. "Why do things look as they do?" asks Koffka in his book, *Gestalt Psychology*. "Because they are what they are," he has his layman answer—an answer that Koffka then proceeds neatly to rebut.

The answer, "Because they are what they are," is another way of saying that there is no problem to be curious about. That there is a problem is perhaps most convincingly demonstrated by those many instances where perception and "physical reality" very obviously do not match and where the mismatch is not attributable simply to random error via lack of precision or sensitivity, but rather to some gross bias, that is, to systematic error, in the observer. The class of perceptual phenomena referred to as *illusions* provides a fascinating collection of examples of this sort.

Once convinced by the compelling nature of illusions, the novice is more ready to accept the notion that if mismatches pose a problem, then matches (between perception and physical reality) must also. The strategy here is analogous to that used by those who study personality, or who make a case for there being a problem to study, by reference to instances of psychopathology by assuming that if abnormality is a problem, then so too is normality.

Of course one can be interested in psychopathology for its own sake and not only as a route to the understanding of the normal personality. One can have a similar interest in illusions. For many of those who first dabbled in this area, illusions were curiosities. This has always remained somewhat the case, though there has also been in the history of psychology a strong interest in illusions and related phenomena as one means to the end of the scientific understanding of perception in general.

In recent years, considerable effort has been expended on the developmental investigation of illusions, especially by the groups led by Werner in this country and Piaget in Geneva.* Out of this work, in particular that of Piaget and his colleagues, has come some rather complex theorizing about perceptual development. Of recent vintage also is the use of certain illusory figures, and responses to them, as indicators of psychopathology.† Finally, some modern theorists have developed hypothetical neural mechanisms for perception, some of the details of which were explicitly designed to handle certain illusory phenomena.‡

The Necker cube has been a favorite illusory figure since it was first described by the geologist, L. A. Necker, in 1832. His report is reproduced in its entirety in the following passage, which is excerpted from a somewhat longer article written in the form of a letter to the editor.

* See, for example, H. Werner and S. Wapner. *Perceptual development.* Worcester: Clark Univ. Press, 1957; J. H. Flavell, *The developmental psychology of Jean Piaget.* Princeton: Van Nostrand, 1963.
† See, for example, G. Spivack and M. Levine. Spiral after-effect as a measure of satiation in brain-injured and normal subjects. *J. Personal,* 1959, **27**, 211–227.
‡ See, for example, W. Köhler and H. Wallach, Figural after-effects. *Proc. Amer. Phil. Soc.,* 1944, **88**, 269–357; J. A. Deutsch, Neurophysiological contrast phenomena and figural aftereffects. *Psychol. Rev.,* 1964, **71**, 19–26.

Louis Albert Necker

On an Apparent Change of Position in a Drawing or Engraved Figure of a Crystal

. . . The object I have now to call your attention to, is an observation which is also of an optical nature, and which has often occurred to me while examining figures and engraved plates of crystalline forms: I mean a sudden and involuntary change in the apparent position of a crystal or solid represented in an engraved figure. What I mean will be more easily understood from the figure annexed. The rhomboid AX is drawn so that the solid angle A should be seen the nearest to the spectator, and the solid angle X the furthest from him, and that the face ACBD should be the foremost, while the face XDC is behind. But in looking repeatedly at the same figure, you will perceive that at times the apparent position of the rhomboid is so changed that the solid angle X will appear the nearest, and the solid angle A the furthest; and that the face ACDB will recede behind the face XDC, which will come forward; which effect gives to the whole solid a quite contrary apparent inclination. I have been a long time at a loss to understand the reason of the apparently accidental and involuntary change which I always witnessed

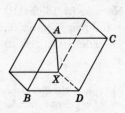

Figure 1

1. A. Necker. Observations on . . . an optical phenomenon which occurs on viewing a figure of a crystal or geometrical solid. *Philosophical Magazine*, 1832, **1** (IIIrd Series), 329–337. The selection is drawn from the last two pages of Necker's letter.

in all sorts of forms in books of crystallography. The only thing I could observe was, that at the time the change took place, a particular sensation was felt in the eye (for it takes place as well when seen with only one eye, as with both eyes), which proved to me that it was an optical, and not merely as I had at first thought a mental, operation which was performed. After, however, a more attentive analysis of the fact, it occurred to me, that it was owing to an involuntary change in the adjustment of the eye for obtaining distinct vision. And that whenever the point of distinct vision on the retina was directed on the angle A, for instance, this angle seen more distinctly than the others was naturally supposed to be nearer and foremost; while the other angles seen indistinctly were supposed to be further, and behind. The reverse took place when the point of distinct vision was brought to bear upon the angle X. This solution being found, I proved that it was the real one by three different ways.

1st, By being able at my will to see the solid in which position I chose, and to make this position vary at pleasure, in looking alternately, with fixed attention, either to the angle A, or to the angle X.

2ndly, While looking steadfastly to the angle A, and seeing the rhomboid in its proper position with the angle A foremost, if without moving either the eye or the figure, I made a convex lens (such as is used in spectacles for long-sightedness,) pass gently from below upwards between the eye and the figure, at the instant when the figure was visible through the glass, the change had taken place, and the solid had assumed the apparent position in which the angle X was the foremost, and that only because, owing to the refraction through the glass, the image of the angle X had come to take the place of the real angle A, and so the point of distinct vision, without being at all moved, had by this means come to bear on the angle X, or rather on its image.

3rdly, If through a hole made with a pin in a card you look at the figure in such a manner that either the angle A or the angle X be hidden, the visible angle will determine the apparent position of the solid, so that this angle will always appear the nearest; it will be impossible to see it any other way, and consequently there will be no change.

What I have said of the solid angles is equally true of the edges,—those edges upon which the axis of the eye or the central hole of the retina are directed will always appear forward; so that now it appears to me certain that this little, at first so puzzling, phaenomenon, depends upon the law of distinct vision.

You surely will draw from all the above communications, many consequences which my ignorance of the subject prevents me from anticipating. You may do what you think most proper with all these observations.

> I remain, my dear Sir, with the kindest regard,
> Ever most sincerely yours,
> L. A. NECKER.

Geneva, May 24, 1832.

* * *

Two years after Necker described the illusion in the passage above, Addams reported in a brief note his observation of what has become known as the "waterfall illusion," or more technically, and more generally, the visual aftereffect of movement (VAM). Note that Addams offers an account of the illusion that refers to events occurring peripherally in the visual system. Recent theorists have sought their explanations of this phenomenon, and related ones, in hypothetical events occurring more centrally in the visual system, particularly in the visual cortex.

The most ingenious, and apparently successful, of the recent attempts to explain the VAM, and the perception of visual movement itself, has been based on the neurophysiological research of Hubel and Wiesel.* These investigators, through electrical recording from single cells in the visual cortex of the cat, have discovered retinal receptive fields that feed into single cortical neurons. These receptive fields contain both excitatory and inhibitory regions; they are so arranged spatially, and many of

---

* D. N. Hubel. The visual cortex of the brain. *Scientific American*, 1963, 209, 54–62.

them so especially sensitive to movement, that they seem well suited to subserve the function of movement perception and to provide the mechanism for the VAM.* There is more to the story than can be told here, but it all began with a chemist looking at a waterfall.

R. Addams

An Account of a Peculiar Optical Phaenomenon

During a recent tour through the Highlands of Scotland, I visited the celebrated Falls of Foyers on the border of Loch Ness, and there noticed the following phaenomenon.

Having steadfastly looked for a few seconds at a particular part of the cascade, admiring the confluence and decussation of the currents forming the liquid drapery of waters, and then suddenly directed my eyes to the left, to observe the vertical face of the sombre age-worn rocks immediately contiguous to the water-fall, I saw the rocky surface as if in motion upwards, and with an apparent velocity equal to that of the descending water, which the moment before had prepared my eyes to behold this singular deception.

The cascade is through a depth of about 70 feet, and my position, as I stood when I made the observation, was nearly on a level with the centre of the fall, being the lowest of the two situations where visitors obtain a view of this copious and never-failing infusion of peat gushing over the giant step and whitening as it flows. My attention was engaged on that part of the

R. Addams. An account of a peculiar optical phaenomenon seen after looking at a moving body, etc. *Philosophical Magazine*, 1834, 5 (IIIrd Series), 373–374.

* R. H. Cormack. Visual movement perception and the visual aftereffect of movement: an empirical and theoretical study. Unpublished doctoral dissertation, University of Cincinnati, 1962.

fall which corresponded with a horizontal plane passing through my eye and the water. The sun was masked by cloud at the time.

I am not aware of any existing explanation of this class of optical phaenomena, and I may be premature in venturing the following.

I conceive the effect to be owing to an involuntary and *unconscious* muscular movement of the eyeball, and thus occasioning a displacement of the images on the retina.

Supposing the eyes to be intently gazing at any point in a transverse plane passing through a vertically moving body, they will naturally and even irresistibly tend to follow the motion of that body; or can the muscular apparatus of the eye maintain a stable equilibrium when the sight is fatigued and bewildered with a rapid change of moving forms before the eye.

Now in the case of the descending water, the eyes, being directed to a particular part in a horizontal section of it, cannot be prevented moving downwards through a small space: every new form in the moving scene invites the eyes to observe, and for that reason to follow it; but the voluntary powers are engaged to raise the axes of the eyes again to the section. This depression of the axes below the *intentional point of sight* seems to be repeated three or four times per second, whilst looking at the waterfall. Then, when the eyes are suddenly turned upon the rock, the muscles, having been brought into a kind of periodic contraction, will perform at least one of these movements after the exciting cause ceases to act; and thus the axes of the eyes, by moving downwards, will occasion a motion of the image of the rock over the retina in a direction from above downwards, and consequently the object giving that image will *appear* to move the contrary way, that is, upwards, agreeably to observation.

The deception, so far as I could judge, seemed to continue for a time equal to the interval of a periodic motion of the eye downwards when looking at the water, and, as before stated, one third or one fourth of a second.

The same kind of phaenomenon may be produced by moving the eye before fixed bodies, and also when the motions are executed horizontally.

I have since been enabled to observe the appearance, with certain peculiar variations, whilst travelling parallel to one side of a narrow valley or lake, and looking across to the other. It takes place when moving in ships in sight of proximate land.

It is also producible by mechanical means, such as by a rapid unrolling of pieces of calico having some pattern or markings on them; and likewise by moving the head up and down, or laterally: but to particularize all the circumstances would make this communication inconveniently long.

* * *

The article to follow is instructive in several ways, of which three deserve special note. First, on a very general level, it illustrates the continuity of science. By his many references to Addams and others, Thompson reveals how dependent the work of the scientist is on that of his predecessors. Thompson's own very clever experiments on the VAM derive much of their meaning from a somewhat vague hypothesis suggested 46 years earlier by Addams. Out of its historical context, Thompson's research would lose much of its impact. And herein, of course, lies the apology for making the work of Thompson and of the other men included in this volume available to the contemporary student of psychology.

Second, in a less general vein, Thompson disposes of the eye-movement explanation of the VAM through a series of simple but convincing experiments. His own hypothesis, itself rather obscure, provides the motivation for the work of some future investigator. Thus, Thompson closes one door, Addam's eye-movement hypothesis, but opens others via his own speculations and thereby helps keep the game of science going.

Third, and very particularly, Thompson, at the end of his article, raises the possibility of meaningful individual differences in susceptibility to the VAM, a theme which has only recently been seriously exploited.

Silvanus Phillips Thompson

Optical Illusions of Motion

There are frequent occasions of conflict between the receptive
faculties of the senses and the reflective faculties of the intellect,
occasions on which the mind, prejudging of the sensation received,
assigns it to a non-existent cause. Of all the senses none is more
frequently the seat of such deceptive judgments than that of
sight; and in the science of physiological optics a very considerable share of attention is claimed by optical illusions. For the
purposes of convenience, we may draw a distinction between
these illusions, which are the direct result of certain properties
or imperfections of the eye as an optical instrument, and those
which arise from obliquities of judgment in interpreting the sensations optically impressed upon the retina of the eye. In practice, however, it is almost impossible to draw a hard-and-fast line
between the two classes of illusions, almost all partaking of both
characters. Thus, for example, it has lately been shown that we
habitually draw geometrical forms too large in the horizontal dimension as compared with their vertical dimension; we draw
oblate ellipses where we intend to draw circles; the explanation of
this being that with our *two* eyes we really *see* spheres as oblate
ellipses. Here is, in fact, an illusion of pure association—yet based
upon the facts of physical and physiological optics. So, again,
certain inequalities in the curvature of the lenses of the eye, producing the optical defect of astigmatism, cause objects that are
horizontal in position to form images at shorter (or longer as the
case may be) distances from the eye than the images of vertical
objects; the result being that, unless the defect is corrected by

S. P. Thompson. Optical illusions of motion. *Brain*, 1880, **3**, 289–298; reprinted in
Pop. Sci. Monthly, 1881, **18**, 519–526.

suitable lenses, vertical and horizontal objects (such as the bars
of a window) do not appear to be at the same distance from the
observer, though really equally remote. This would, at first sight,
appear to be a purely physical illusion, and not psychological.
Nevertheless, a little consideration will show that since our perception of distance is a psychological factor in the case, and that
this perception is based in part upon the muscular sensations of
adjustment of the lenses of the eye to exact focus, the illusion is
one which has a psychological as well as a physical *raison d'être*.
Again, take some illusions ordinarily supposed to be one purely
of mental association: the common illusion of every day, that the
sun or moon when a few degrees from the horizon looks larger
than when high in the sky, appears at first sight to be due simply
to the fact that when the orb is near the horizon the distant
objects upon that horizon whose size we know, or can judge of,
appear relatively small, and the sun's disk relatively large—in
fact, that the illusion is one purely of association of ideas. Nevertheless, when we look a little closer into the matter, we find that
our simplest conceptions of angular or apparent magnitude are
very closely bound up with, if not directly due to, the sensations
of muscular fatigue in moving the eyeball or head so as to bring
the successive parts of the object into the center of vision.

Hence, although optical illusions are of many diverse kinds—
illusions of color, illusions of form, illusions of size, illusions of
distance, illusions of solidity, and illusions of motion—they have all
to be considered from the twofold standpoint, the purely optical
and the psychological.

For some months the writer of this article was engaged upon
a study of one set of optical illusions, namely, the illusions of
motion, and a number of observations, collected at intervals over
several years, have been added by him to the stock of knowledge
previously gleaned by Brewster, Wheatstone, Faraday, Plateau,
and others. Brewster made a number of observations, in the early
days of railways, on the various illusions which can be found by
watching objects from a moving train; Wheatstone investigated
a curious case of apparent fluttering motion at the border of two
brightly illuminated colored surfaces—due probably to the attempt
of the unachromatic eye to obtain fruitlessly a distinct focus of

the border-line between the unequally refrangible colors—known as the illusion of the "Fluttering Hearts"; Faraday investigated the illusions produced by intermittent views of moving objects, since developed in the phenakistiscope and zoetrope, and kindred toys, and due to persistence of visual impressions. Brewster, moreover, drew attention to the existence of another class of illusions—illusions of subjective complementary motion—the typical case of which occurs also in railway-traveling. After looking out of the window at the pebbles and other objects lying beside the line, as they pass before the eyes, let the eyes be closed suddenly, when there will at once be perceived an apparent motion in the opposite sense, undistinguishable forms and patches of light seeming to rush past the blank field. This was recorded by Sir David in 1848, and the phenomenon was referred by him to a subjective complementary motion going on simultaneously, and so causing a compensation of the impressions moving over the retina. A kindred phenomenon had been even earlier noted by R. Addams, who, in 1834, narrated how, after looking for some time at a waterfall and then at the water-worn rocks immediately contiguous, he saw the rocky surface as if in motion upward with an apparent velocity equal to that of the descending water. This he ascribed to an unconscious slipping of the inferior and superior recti muscles of the eyeballs, which he thought occurred while watching the falling water, and which he supposed to continue unconsciously after the gaze had been transferred to stationary objects. This explanation differs from the one offered by Brewster, namely, that there was a subjective *opposite* movement going on simultaneously, so causing a compensation of the impressions moving over the retina. Brewster's hypothesis is, indeed, extremely vague, and is neither physical nor psychological in any exact sense. If understood physically, it means that there is actually motion in the retina itself, which is hardly conceivable, since the structure of the rods and cones almost precludes even any idea of vibration, or of propagation of waves of motion by vibration, much less any movements of them as a whole. And, if the explanation is intended as a psychological one, something further is needful before the principle of compensation here laid down could become intelligible.

The first experiments made by the writer of this article upon illusions of motion arose from a casual observation in 1876. He had been preparing, for the purpose of testing astigmatism, a set of concentric circles in black and white, such as those shown in Fig. 1. Happening to shake the sheet on which the circles were drawn, he noticed an apparent motion of rotation to be set up. The illusion is easily produced by imparting to the pattern a slight motion of the same character as that adopted in *rinsing* out a pail, but with a very minute radius of motion. All the circles will appear to rotate with the same angular velocity as that imparted. Now, undoubtedly the persistence of visual impressions has a good deal to do with the production of this illusion, which, by the way, succeeds best when the circles make from two to four turns in a second, and when the radius of the imparted motion is equal to the thickness of one ring, so that each black or white band is displaced through a distance equal to its own width in all directions successively. Nevertheless, the persistence of

Figure 1

visual impressions will not explain all the facts of this curious illusion: for, in the first place, it is found that for increasing distances from the eye the concentric rings must be made wider if the illusion is to succeed; there being apparently one particular magnitude of their images on the retina which favors the production of the illusion. Again, if two such "strobic circles" (as I have called them) are printed side by side on one card, that set of circles seems to turn most effectively at which the eye is *not* looking. On stopping the "rinsing motion" suddenly, there appears to be, for an instant, a reverse motion. Finally, if a set of circles is "rotated" while another set lies motionless within the field of view, the second set will appear to rotate when the first are "rotated" in the manner described above. It is possible, also, to have a number of such apparent motions going on at once independently in one field of view. Fig. 2 shows a compound pattern, containing an interior set of concentric circles and six internally-toothed wheels. When a very minute "rinsing" motion is imparted to this figure, the circles appear to whirl round while the toothed-wheels work slowly backward, moving through one tooth while the circles whirl round once. Here, again, persistence of vision is concerned—but not exclusively.

Figure 2

Dr. Emile Javal, the able director of the Ophthalmological Laboratory of the Sorbonne, has recently advanced an explanation of these illusions different from that adopted by the writer, and in substance identical with that advanced by R. Addams in the case of the waterfall illusion. He avers that the eye, in order to observe a movement, follows the moving body for an instant and then suddenly slips back; that this oscillation, frequently repeated, is associated with a sensation of motion in the particular direction in question; and that when the eye is subsequently directed to a stationary object it continues the habit of thus oscillating, causing the observer to attribute to the object a velocity of opposite sign to that just observed. M. Javal alleges in support of this view the appearance presented in the ophthalmoscope of the retina of a person affected with *nystagmus*. This affection consists in continual rapid involuntary movements to and fro of the eye. The retina, under these circumstances, appears to be animated with a vibratory motion which M. Javal declares to be identical in character with the apparent movements of the circles. In another place, Mr. Javal has endeavored to prove that the interior and exterior recti muscles of the eyeball are more prone to this slipping than are the superior and inferior recti, and that these illusions of complementary motion succeed better for motions in an horizontal sense than for vertical and oblique motions. My own experience, and that of other observers, admits of no such conclusion being drawn.

An experiment of Brewster's, which the writer tried without knowing at the time that Brewster had employed it, has an important bearing on the muscular-slipping theory. A disk marked out into black and white sectors, as in Fig. 3, was caused to rotate at about one revolution per second, so that the separate sensations of black and white were not confused. The eye was steadily directed for twenty or thirty seconds at the central point, and then the gaze was suddenly turned upon some fixed objects, or at a distant landscape. For two or three seconds a hazy rotation is noticed at the center of the field of vision. Now, if the muscular-slipping theory holds good, the complementary movement of rotation must be due to a slipping of the whole of the muscles of the eyeball, and would affect objects all over the field of vision with an equal angular velocity. This is not the case, the

Figure 3   Figure 4

apparent complementary rotation being confined to the central field, and with apparent angular velocities increasing toward the center of vision. Furthermore, I have arranged two such disks so that they could be simultaneously in the field of view while rotating in opposite directions. When the gaze was directed first at a point between them and then at fixed objects, there appeared to be two portions of the field of view rotating, and animated with rotations in opposed senses. Clearly, the eye can not' slip round in opposite directions at the same time. In all these illusions, moreover, it is found that this illusory complementary motion only occurs over limited parts of the field of view—namely, those which correspond to the portions of the retina which previously received the moving images. Thus, if a waterfall be looked at—as in Addams's observation—the upward illusory aftermotion is confined to a vertical streak across the field of vision. This fact alone is sufficient to negative the theory of muscular slip.

The final test to which I have appealed is, if possible, even more conclusive. It is probably a familiar observation that the end of the last carriage of a retreating railway-train appears to shrink down smaller and smaller as it subtends a decreasing angular magnitude in the field of view. After looking at this motion for a sufficient number of seconds to fatigue the eye, stationary objects appear to be expanding. To produce this illusion more effectually, I take a disk like that shown in Fig. 4 (the figure is quarter actual size), marked out in spirals of white and black. If this is slowly rotated—say at about one revolution in two seconds—the whole pattern appears either to be running into, or running out of, the center of the disk: there is a motion of convergence or divergence, according to the sense of the rotation. Let the disk be turned so as to cause an apparent convergence from all sides to the center, and let the eye steadily watch the center for about a minute, or until the fatigue becomes almost unendurable. Then look at any fixed object—the pattern of the wall-paper, or the dial of a clock—the object so regarded will for some two, or three, or more seconds, appear to be expanding from the center outward. The effect is still more startling if the object thus viewed be the face of a familiar friend. It is quite evident that the eyeball can not slip in all directions at once.

I have, therefore, somewhat reluctantly been led to propound an explanation for these illusions, embodying the theory of them in an empirical law based upon the physical fact of retinal fatigue, and on the psychological fact of association of contrasts. It is as follows: *The retina ceases to perceive as a motion a steady succession of images that pass over a particular region for a sufficient time to induce fatigue; and, on a portion of the retina so affected, the image of a body not in motion appears by contrast to be moving in a complementary direction.* This law is precisely similar to that of the complementary subjective colors seen after fatiguing the retina by the image of a colored body. Similar laws of physico-psychological after-effects are abundant. A steady sound of one constant pitch ceases to be heard until we become aware of it by its cessation. A steady light of one color, such as the yellow light of gas-flames, ceases to be noticed as a yellow light until some other color-sensation break the illusion. The same is true of smells, of tastes, of the sensations of temperature, of the sensation of rotation after a waltz, and of many others. All these are probably only different instances of the operation of some much more general physico-psychological law. It is quite consonant with these kindred phenomena that, when any region of the retina is affected by an image of objects moving steadily across the corresponding portion of the field of view in any given direction, that portion of the retina gradually loses consciousness of the motion, and perceives it only as a steady sensation, or as one of approximate rest. When, however, an object really at rest is looked at, the associative faculty seizes upon the contrast in the sensations affecting that region, and interprets the new sensation by imputing a motion in the opposite sense to the objects occupying the corresponding portion of the field of vision. I have proposed to give to the empirical law expressing these matters the name of the *law of subjective complementary motion*.

It is impossible to quit the subject without pointing out two lines of thought suggested by that which has been advanced.

Firstly, it is conceivable that the explanation here propounded may at some future time be superseded by a better hypothesis of a more purely physical character. Suppose, for example, that it could be shown—what I have reason to suspect, but have been foiled in all attempts to prove in any experimental fashion—that the eye has the power of altering at will the actual size of the retinal images by a double muscular adjustment between the magnifying power of the lenses of the eye and the distance of their equivalent optical center from the surface of the retina, such a fact, once established, would entirely cut away the significance of my crucial test with the rotating spirals; and the apparent expansions and contractions of objects would be merely due to the continuous attempts of the eye to retain the retinal images of one constant size. If this were so (though I have failed in every kind of attempt to devise some satisfactory test), it might also explain one little matter that is still very mysterious and unexplainable, namely, that in these illusions of expansion and contraction the changes of apparent magnitude often appear to take place by discontinuous jumps rather than by steady motions.

Secondly, it is found that these different illusions affect different individuals with very different degrees of success, some persons being much more sensitive than others to the after-workings of the subjective motion; and, indeed, there are individuals in whose case it is almost impossible to produce the illusions. Doubtless some of these differences may be accounted for by defects of vision, astigmatism, achromatopsy, myopy, and the

like. But there is also a time-element in the case which varies
very greatly with individuals, and even varies with the nervous
states of the same individual. And this suggests the further
thought that a careful comparison of individuals relatively to
their illusion-capacity might elicit some interesting and perhaps
valuable facts concerning the relation between the states of brain-
organization and the sensations of the more highly specialized
organs of sense.

* * *

As pointed out in the opening remarks of this chapter, illusions
pose no special problem for perceptual theory; they require no
more, nor no less explanation than any other class of perceptual
phenomena. Ernst Mach, physicist-philosopher-psychologist,
makes this same point in slightly different terms in the following
very brief excerpt.

. . . The expression "sense-illusion" proves that we are not yet
fully conscious, or at least have not yet deemed it necessary to
incorporate the fact into our ordinary language, *that the senses
represent things neither wrongly nor correctly.* All that can be
truly said of the sense-organs is, that, *under different circumstances
they produce different sensations and perceptions.* As these "circumstances," now, are extremely various in character, being partly
external (inherent in the objects), partly internal (inherent in
the sensory organs), and partly interior (having their activity in
the central organs), it can sometimes appear, when we only notice
the external circumstances, as if the organ acted differently under
the same conditions. And it is customary to call the unusual effects,
deceptions or illusions.*

Mach's contribution to the field of perception is not only philosophical, but also empirical. The latter aspect of his work is
no better illustrated than in his research on the perception of

---

* E. Mach. *The analysis of sensations.* 1914, Footnote, p. 10. See page 94
for full citation.

contour, of which the well-known "Mach bands" or "Mach rings" are a special and dramatic case. This work is described in the passage below. Note especially the power achieved through the use of mathematical analysis—an approach that is so characteristic of the physicist-psychologists—Mach, Helmholtz, Fechner, and others. Contemporary theorizing in perception, as well as in other areas of psychology, is, of course, liberally colored by the mathematical tint.*

Ernst Mach

On Contours

The deviation of a sensation from the mean of the adjacent sensations is always noticeable, and exacts a special effort on the part of the sense-organ. Every new turn of a curve, every projection or depression of a surface, involves a deviation of some space-sensation from the mean of the surrounding field on which the attention is directed. The plane is distinguished physiologically by the fact that this deviation from the mean is a minimum, or for each point in particular $= 0$. In looking through a stereoscope at a spotted surface, the separate images of which have not yet been combined into a binocular image, we experience a peculiarly agreeable impression when the whole is suddenly flattened out into a plane. The aesthetic impressions produced by the circle and the sphere seem to have their source mainly in the fact that the above-mentioned deviation from the mean is the same for all points.

E. Mach. *The analysis of sensations and the relation of the physical to the psychical.* Translated from the 1st German edition by C. M. Williams; revised and supplemented from the 5th German edition (1906) by S. Waterlow. Chicago: Open Court, 1914. The first German edition was published in 1886 and first translated into English in 1897. This selection is taken from pp. 215–220 of the Williams-Waterlow translation.

* See G. A. Miller. *Mathematics and psychology.* New York: Wiley, 1964.

That the deviation from the mean of the environment plays a rôle in light-sensation I pointed out many years ago. If a row of black and white sectors, such as are shown in [the accompanying figure], be painted on a strip of paper $A\,A\,B\,B$, and this be then wrapped about a cylinder the axis of which is parallel to AB, there will be produced, on the rapid rotation of the cylinder, a grey field with increasing illumination from B to A, in which, however, a brighter line $\alpha\,\alpha$, and a darker line $\beta\,\beta$, make their appearance. The points which correspond to the indentations α are not physically brighter than the neighboring parts, but their light-intensity exceeds the mean intensity of the immediately adjacent parts, while, on the other hand, the light-intensity at β falls short of the mean intensity of the adjacent parts. This deviation from the mean is thus distinctly felt, and accordingly imposes a special burden upon the organ of sight. On the other hand a continuous change in brightness is scarcely noticed, as long as the brightness of each particular point corresponds to the mean of the adjacent points. Long ago I drew attention to the important teleological bearing of this fact on the saliency and the delimitation of objects. . . . Small differences are slurred over by the retina, and larger differences stand out with disproportionate clearness. The retina schematizes and caricatures. At an even earlier period the important part which outlines play in vision had been noticed by Panum.

A series of very various experiments, of which that represented in [the figure] is one of the simplest, led me to the conclusion that the illumination of a position on the retina is felt in proportion to its deviation from the mean of the illuminations of the adjacent positions. The value of the retinal positions in deter-

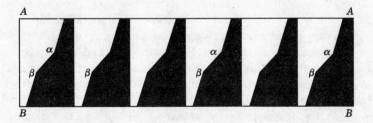

mining this mean is to be conceived as rapidly decreasing with their distance from the position under consideration, a fact which of course can only be explained as depending on an organic reciprocal action of the retinal elements on one another. Let $i = f(x, y)$ be the intensity of illumination of the retina with reference to a system of co-ordinates (XY); then the mean value determining the intensity for a given position may be symbolically represented as approximately

$$i + \frac{m}{2}\left(\frac{\partial^2 i}{\partial x^2} + \frac{\partial^2 i}{\partial y^2}\right)$$

where m is constant, and the radii of all curves of the surface f (x, y) are taken as large in proportion to the distance at which the retinal positions are still perceptibly influenced. Now according as $\left(\frac{\partial^2 i}{\partial x^2} + \frac{\partial^2 i}{\partial y^2}\right)$ is positive or negative, the position on the retina experiences a darker or a brighter sensation respectively than it does under equal illumination of the adjacent positions with the intensity corresponding to itself. If the surface $f(x, y)$ has edges and indentations, $\left(\frac{\partial^2 i}{\partial x^2} + \frac{\partial^2 i}{\partial y^2}\right)$ becomes infinite, and the formula is useless. In this case, however, a marked increase of darkness or brightness corresponds to the indentation, though of course not an infinite increase or decrease. The increase or decrease, again, are not defined by a hard and fast line, but fade gradually away, as we should expect from the principle of deviation from the mean. For the retina consists, not of sensitive points, but of an infinite number of sensitive elements of finite extension. As regards the law of the reciprocal action of these elements, we still do not know it accurately enough to enable us to determine precisely the phenomena of this special case.

It is easy to go wrong in judging of the objective distribution of light according to the subjective impression, and consequently a knowledge of the above-mentioned law of contrast is important even for purely physical researches. Thus Grimaldi was deceived by a phenomenon of this kind. We come across the same phenomenon in the investigation of shadows, and of spectral absorption, and in countless other cases. Peculiar circumstances prevented my papers on this subject from becoming generally known, and the relevant facts were discovered for the second time thirty years later.

It may seem surprising that, in addition to i, the second differential quotients of i, but not the first, $\dfrac{\partial i}{\partial x}$, $\dfrac{\partial i}{\partial y}$, seem to influence the sensation of brightness. We scarcely notice a regular and continuous rise in the intensity of illumination of a surface,—for instance, in the direction x,—and special devices are necessary to convince one that there is a rise. On the other hand, these first differential quotients exercise an influence on the modelling, on the plastic quality, of the surface seen.

4

Spatial Localization

As far as biological adaptation is concerned, one of the most significant aspects of an object is its location relative to that of the observing organism. This is true whatever the sense modality—visual, auditory, tactual—by which information about the existence of the object is transmitted to the organism. It is not enough that a dog, being bitten by a flea, experience a sensation of a certain quality (pain, itchiness), intensity, and duration; if the dog is to do something about that flea, he must be able fairly accurately to localize the sensation on the surface of his body and thereby locate his tormentor.

Sounds come to us not only as high or low pitched, loud or soft, pleasant or unpleasant, long or short, but also as emanating from a particular locus. How accurately, and by what means, we can localize sounds represent problems for empirical research, but it seems unquestionable that a significant aspect of auditory experience relates to the phenomenal location of its origin.

Of all the modalities, smell is perhaps the least endowed with spatiality. One can certainly localize the source of an odor with considerable accuracy if adequately provoked (is it coming from that chemical factory we are passing in the car or from baby's diaper?), but locus is not nearly so compelling with smelling as it is with tactual, auditory, and especially visual sensations.

Visual objects are almost invariably localized, though not always accurately, in all three dimensions of physical space. (I see two cardinals on a tree outside my office window; the male is perched to the left of the female and is somewhat higher up; both are closer to me than the dog that is also watching them from the sidewalk behind the tree.) Indeed, the location of a visual object frequently precedes the perception of any of its other attributes, such as shape, color, or size.

As might be expected from its biological significance and phenomenal intrusiveness, spatial localization has been a topic of considerable interest to students of perception. This topic, perhaps more than any other in the area of perception, has been a major meeting ground of those diverse disciplines—philosophy, physics, physiology, psychology—that have dealt with the problem of perception. And as usual, localization in the visual mode has been the main object of inquiry.

The host of issues that have emerged in the study of visual spatial localization can be, for convenience, categorized into two broad classes—those relating to localization in two dimensions, up-down, left-right, that is, *bidimensional* localization—and those involving the third dimension of depth or distance, that is, *tridimensional* localization. The distinction is analogous to that between plane and solid geometry, where the two topics are intimately related, but can be, and have been, treated separately.

Every visual object, plane or solid, casts a two-dimensional image on the retina, which is the light-sensitive surface on the back of the eye. As far as the localization of plane objects is concerned, then, the receptor mechanism is of the same dimensionality as the object to be localized. Not that this one-to-one correspondence between the geometry of plane objects and that of the retina solves all the problems of bidimensional localization, but it does highlight the special problem of tridimensional localization: how is information about the third spatial dimension received and transmitted by a receptive surface of only two dimensions?

Answers to the questions about the mechanisms of bi- and tridimensional visual localization have typically taken the form of specifying "cues" for each of the two classes of perceptual event. Further controversy then arises over the genesis of these cues. Are they native? That is, is the organism endowed at birth with the necessary apparatus (physiological or "mental," depending on the orientation of the theorist) to utilize these cues? Or is their utilization the product of experience? Does the organism learn to appreciate the significance of these cues through his sensory encounters, via visual and also other modalities, with objects? Here, of course, we run into the perennial, and to many artificial and fruitless, nativism-empiricism controversy. "Artificial" because on close scrutiny there seem to have been no unambivalent empiricists, nor any complete nativists, nor would either position in the extreme be tenable; "fruitless" because artificial controversies, like neurotic conflicts, allow of no satisfactory solution. But fruitful or fruitless, the nativism-empiricism controversy comprises a large portion of the efforts of nineteenth century investigators of perception and therefore deserves the space it is allotted in this chapter.

Considerable knowledge about the structure of the eye, in relation to the problem of localization, was already available prior to the nineteenth century. For example, Descartes in 1637 showed that an image of an object being viewed is formed at the back of the eye, where the retina is located, thus confirming by experiment an hypothesis proposed earlier by the astronomer Kepler. Kepler had also implicated the lens as the focussing mechanism, though he had incorrectly believed that it performed this function by changing its distance from the retina as object distance changed, whereas in fact the lens accomplishes its work by changing shape. This latter idea was supported by some of Young's research (as described in Chapter 2) and championed by Helmholtz against opposition as formidable as Müller. At any rate, it became clear by the middle of the nineteenth century that an image of an object being viewed is formed on the retina as a two-dimensional array, and that this retinal image contains the information relative to the object's directionality. Moreover, since lens shape changed with object distance, in order to maintain a clearly focussed retinal image, it becomes conceivable that this process of *accommodation*, which as Helmholtz argued involved muscular action, might provide cues about the object's distance from the observer. Here, then, lay the basis for one line of research on the perception of object distance that was actively pursued in the nineteenth century.

Accommodation is a reflexive response that assures a clearly focussed retinal image for objects at varying distances from the observer. Another reflexive response activated by varying object distance is *convergence,* the process whereby the two eyes rotate, in concert, about the horizontal axis, so as to maintain direct fixation on objects regardless of their distance. With fixation on an object at "infinite" distance (beyond about 6 meters) the two eyes are so positioned that a hypothetical straight line through the fovea and pupil of the right eye to the object would be essentially parallel to a similar line from the left eye. As the object distance decreases, the two eyes converge, as do the two hypothetical lines, which meet at the object.

Again, since convergence is accomplished through muscular activity, which in turn, like other muscular activity, is accompanied by proprioceptive feedback, it becomes another potential source of cues to object distance, at least for objects closer than 6 meters. Such an hypothesis was suggested by Descartes and formed one of the bases for Berkeley's classic "An Essay Towards a New Theory of Vision," published in 1709 and considered by Boring to be the first truly psychological monograph.

Convergence, like accommodation, was also the object of considerable research efforts in the nineteenth century. The outcome of these experiments seemed to be that both processes, accommodation and convergence, do provide distance cues, though limited and not very powerful ones, and that neither was necessary to the perception of distance.

Of course, there is a large number of other candidates for the role of providing distance cues, for example, linear and aerial perspective, interposition, movement parallax, and others; many of these were known to artists, such as Leonardo, who used them, where feasible on a flat surface, to create the "illusion" of depth in their paintings, and most of them are known to the reader of any good text in introductory psychology. Chief among these many clues is one that results from binocular parallax, that is, *retinal disparity,* a discovery of Sir Charles Wheatstone and the topic of the second selection in this chapter. For purposes of preserving chronology, the passage by Wheatstone is preceded by one from the work of Thomas Brown, theologian and philosopher, and member of the Scottish School of psychology.

In the excerpt below, Brown presents his argument that the perception of solidity, distance, extension, and breadth through the tactual and kinesthetic modes is not a primary, that is, native, attribute of those modes, but rather is derived from experience and dependent for its development on the more primitive perception of temporal succession. This is a strongly empiricist approach to space perception, and Brown has worked out the details of his argument with admirable clarity. Of particular interest in Brown's writing is the attention he pays to muscular activity, especially as a source of sensory experience. This is an emphasis which wanes and waxes periodically in the history of psychology. It will come up again in various forms in Chapter 6 of this volume, along with another brief excerpt from Thomas Brown.

Thomas Brown

Perception of Extension

. . . The proof, that our perception of *extension* by *touch*, is not *an original and immediate perception of that sense,* is altogether independent of the success of any endeavour which may be made, to discover the elements of the compound perception. It would not be *less true,* that touch does *not* afford it, though we should be incapable of pointing out any *other* source, from which it can be supposed to be derived. Of the difficulty of the attempt, and the caution with which we should venture to form any conclusion on the subject, I have already spoken. But the analysis, difficult as it is, is too interesting not to be attempted, even at the *risk,* or perhaps I should rather say, with the *very great probability,* of failure.

T. Brown. *Lectures on the philosophy of the human mind.* In four volumes. Edinburgh: W. & C. Tait, 1820. This selection is taken from Lecture XXIV in the first volume.

In such an analysis, however, though we are to proceed with the greatest caution, it may be necessary to warn you, that it is a part of this very caution, not to be easily terrified, by the appearance of paradox, which the result of our analysis may present. This appearance we may be certain, that any analysis which is at all accurate *must* present, because the very object of the analysis is to shew, that sensations, which appear simple and direct, are *not* simple,—that our senses, in short, are *not* fitted, of themselves, to convey that information, which they now appear, and through the whole course of our *memory* have appeared to us, *instantly* to convey. It is very far, indeed from following, as a necessary consequence, that every analysis of our sensations which affords a paradoxical result, is, therefore, a just one—for error may be extravagant in *appearance* as well as in *reality*. But it *may* truly be regarded as a necessary consequence, that every accurate and original analysis of our *sensations must* afford a result, that, as first stated, will appear paradoxical.

To those who are wholly unacquainted with the theory of vision, nothing certainly can seem, as first stated, more absurd than the assertion, that we see, not with our eyes merely, but chiefly by the medium of another organ, which the blind possess in as great perfection as ourselves, and which, at the moment of vision, may perhaps be absolutely at rest. It must not surprise you, therefore, though the element which seems to me to form the most important constituent of our notion of extension should in like manner, as first stated to you, seem a very unlikely one.

This element is our feeling of *succession,* or *time,*—a feeling, which, necessarily, involves the notion of *divisibility* or series of parts, that is so essential a constituent of our more complex notion of *matter,*—and to which notion of continuous divisibility, if the notion of resistance be added, it is scarcely possible for us to imagine, that we should not have acquired, by this union, the very notion of physical extension,—*that which has parts, and that which resists our effort to grasp it.*

That *memory* is a part of our mental constitution, and that we are thus capable of thinking of a *series of feelings,* as *successive to each other,* the experience of every moment teaches us sufficiently. This succession frequently repeated, *suggests immedi-*

ately, or *implies* the notion of *length,* not *metaphorically,* as is commonly said, but as *absolutely* as extension itself: and, the *greater the number* of the successive feelings may have been, the greater does this length appear. It is *not* possible for us to look back on the years of our life, since they form truly a progressive *series,* without regarding them as a *sort of length,* which is *more distinct* indeed, the *nearer* the succession of feelings may be to the moment at which we consider them, but which, however remote, is still felt by us as *one continued length,* in the same manner, as when, after a journey of many hundred miles, we look back, in our memory, on the distance over which we have passed, we see, as it were, a long track of which *some* parts, *particularly the nearer parts,* are sufficiently *distinct,* but of which the rest seems *lost* in a sort of *distant obscurity.* The line of our long journeying —or, in other words, that almost immeasurable line of plains, hills, declivities, marshes, bridges, woods,—to endeavour to comprehend which in our thought, seems an effort as fatiguing as the very journey itself—we know well, can be *divided* into those *various* parts:—and, in like manner, the *progressive line of time*—or, in other words, the *continued succession,* of which the joy, the hope, the fragrance, the regret, the melody, the fear, and innumerable other affections of the mind, were *parts,* we feel that we can mentally *divide* into those separate portions of the train. Continuous *length* and *divisibility,* those great elementary notions of space, and of all that space contains, are thus found in *every succession of our feelings.* There is no language in which *time* is not described as long or short,—not from any metaphor—for no *mere arbitrary* metaphor can be thus *universal,* and *inevitable,* as a form of human thought—but because it is truly impossible for us to consider *succession, without this notion of progressive divisibility attached to it:* and it appears to us as absurd to suppose, that by *adding,* to our retrospect of a week, the events of the month preceding, we do not truly *lengthen* the succession, as it would be to suppose, that we do not *lengthen* the line of actual distance, by adding, to the few last stages of a long journey, the *many* stages that preceded it.

It is this *spreading out of life* into a long expanse, which allows man to create, as it were, *his own world.* He cannot change, in-

deed, the *scene of external things*. But this may be said, in one
sense, to be the residence only of his *corporeal part*. It is the *moral
scene* in which the *spirit* truly *dwells;* and *this* adapts itself, with
harmonious loveliness, or with *horror* as *suitable,* to the character
of its *pure* or *guilty inhabitant.* If but a *single moment of life,—*
a physical *point,* as it were, of the long line—could be reviewed
at once, conscience would have little power of retribution. But he
who has lived, *as man should live,* is permitted to enjoy that best
happiness *which man can enjoy,*—to behold, in one continued
series, those years of benevolent wishes or of heroic suffering,
which are at once his *merit* and his *reward.* He is *surrounded* by
his own pure thoughts and actions, which, from the most remote
distance, seem to shine upon him wherever his glance can reach;
as in some climate of perpetual summer, in which the inhabitant
sees nothing but fruits and blossoms, and inhales only fragrance,
and sunshine, and delight. It is in a moral climate as serene and
cloudless, that the destined inhabitant of a still nobler world
moves on, in that glorious track, which has *heaven before,* and
virtue and tranquillity behind;—and in which it is scarcely possible to distinguish, in the immortal career, when the *earthly* part
has ceased, and the *heavenly* begins.

Is it in *metaphor* only, that a youth and maturity, and old age
of guilt, seem to *stretch themselves out* in almost endless *extent,*
to that eye which, with all its shuddering reluctance, is still *con-
demned* to *gaze* on them,—when, after the long retrospect seems
finished, some fraud, or excess, or oppression, *still rises* and adds
to the *dreadful line*—and when eternity itself, in all the horrors
which it presents, seems only a still longer line of the same dreadful species, that admits of no other measure, than the continued
sufferings, and remembrance, and terrors that compose it! . . .

By those, who can look back on years that are *long past,* and
yet say, that the *continued progress,* or the *length* and the *short-
ness* of time, are only *metaphorical* expressions, it might be said,
with equal justness, that the roundness of a sphere, is a metaphor,
or the angularity of a cube. We do not more truly *consider* the one
as *angular* and the other as *round,* than we consider the *time* to
be continuously *progressive,* in which we considered, first the one
figure, and then the *other,* and inquired into the properties of each.

That which is progressive must have *parts*. Time, or succession, then involves the very notions of *longitudinal extension* and *divisibility*, and involves these, *without the notion of any thing external to the mind itself;*—for, though the mind of man had been susceptible only of *joy, grief, fear, hope*, and the other varieties of *internal feeling*, WITHOUT the possibility of being *affected by external things*, he would still have been capable of considering these feelings, as *successive* to each other, in a *long continued progression, divisible* into *separate parts*. The notions of *length*, then, and of *divisibility*, are not confined to *external things*, but are *involved*, in that very memory, by which we consider the series of the past, —not in the memory of distant events only, but in those first *successions* of feeling, by which the mind originally became conscious of its own permanence and identity. The *notion* of *time*, then, is precisely *coeval* with that of the *mind itself;* since it is implied in the knowledge of succession, by which alone, in the manner formerly explained to you, the mind acquires the knowledge of its own reality, as something more than the mere sensation of the present moment.

Conceiving the notion of *time*, therefore, that is to say of feelings past and present, to be thus one of the earliest *notions* which the infant mind can form, so as precede its *notions* of external things, and to *involve* the notions of *length* and *divisibility*, I am inclined to *reverse* exactly the process commonly supposed; and, instead of deriving the measure of *time* from *extension*, to derive the knowledge and original measure of extension from time. That one notion or feeling of the mind may be united indissolubly with other feelings, with which it has frequently coexisted, and to which, but for this coexistence, it would seem to have no common relation, is sufficiently shown by those phenomena of vision to which I have already so frequently alluded.

In what manner, however, is the notion of *time peculiarly* associated with the *simple sensation* of *touch*, so as to form, with it, the *perception* of *extension?* We are able, in the theory of *vision*, to point out the coexistence of sensations which produce the *subsequent union;* that renders the perception of distance apparently *immediate*. If a similar coexistence of the original *sensations of touch*, with the notion of *continued and divisible succession*, cannot be pointed out in the present case, the opinion, which asserts it, must be considered merely as a wild and extravagant conjecture.

The source of such a coexistence is not merely *to be found,* but is at least *as obvious,* as *that* which is universally admitted in the case of *vision.*

Before I proceed, however, to state to you, in what way I conceive the notion to be acquired, I must again warn you of the necessity of banishing, as much as possible, from your view of the mind of the infant in this early process, all those notions of external things, which we are so apt to regard as almost *original* in the mind, because we do not remember the time, when they rose in our own. As we know well, that there are external things, of a certain form, acting on our organs, which are also of a certain form, it seems so very simple a process, to perceive *extension*—that is to say, to know that there exist without us those external forms, which really exist—that to endeavour to discover the mode, in which extension, that now appears so obvious a quality of external things, is perceived by us, seems to be a needless search, at a distance, for what is already before our very eyes. And it will be allowed, that all this would, indeed, be very easy to a mind like ours, after the acquisitions of knowledge which it has made; but the difficulty of the very question is, how the mind of the infant makes these acquisitions, so as to *become* like ours. You must not think of a mind, that has any knowledge of things external, even of its own bodily organs, but of a mind simply affected with certain feelings, and having nothing but these feelings to lead it to the knowledge of things without.

To proceed, then,—The hand is the great organ of touch. It is composed of various articulations, that are easily moveable, so as to adapt it readily to changes of shape, in accommodation to the shape of the bodies which it grasps. If we *shut* our hand *gradually,* or *open* it *gradually,* we find a *certain series* of feelings, varying with each degree of the opening or closing, and giving the notion of *succession* of a *certain length.* In like manner, if we gradually extend our *arms,* in various directions, or bring them nearer to us again, we find, that each degree of the motion is accompanied with a feeling that is distinct, so as to render us completely conscious of the progression. The gradual closing of the hand, therefore, must necessarily give a succession of feelings,—a succession, which, of itself, might, or rather *must,* furnish the notion of length, in the manner before stated, the length being different, according to the degree of the closing; and the gradual stretching out of the arm gives a succession of feelings, which, in like manner, must furnish the notion of length,—the length being different according to the degree of the stretching of the arm. To those who have had opportunities of observing infants, I need not say, *how much use,* or rather what constant use, the future inquirer makes of his *little fingers and arms;* by the frequent contraction of which, and the consequent renewal of the series of feelings involved in each gradual contraction, he cannot fail to become so well acquainted with the *progress,* as to distinguish *each degree of contraction,* and, at last, after innumerable repetitions, to associate with each degree the *notion of a certain length of succession.* The particular contraction, therefore, when thus often repeated, becomes the *representative of a certain length,* in the same manner as shades of colour, in vision, become ultimately *representative of distance,*—the same principle of association, which forms the combination in the one case, operating equally in the other.

In these circumstances of *acquired knowledge,*—after the series of muscular feelings, in the voluntary closing of the hand, has become so familiar, that the whole series is anticipated and expected, as soon as the motion has begun,—when a *ball,* or any other substance, is placed for the first time in the infant's hand, he feels that he can no longer perform the usual contraction,—or, in other words, since he does not fancy that he has muscles which are contracted, he feels that the usual series of sensations does not follow his will to renew it,—he knows *how much* of the accustomed succession is still *remaining;* and the notion of *this particular length,* which was expected, and interrupted by a new sensation, is thus associated with the *particular tactual feeling* excited by the pressure of the ball,—the greater or less magnitude of the ball preventing a greater or less portion of the series of feelings in the accustomed contraction. By the frequent repetition of this *tactual feeling,* as associated *with that feeling, which attends a certain progress of contraction,* the two feelings at last flow together, as in the acquired perceptions of vision; and when the process has been repeated with various bodies innumerable times, it becomes, at last, as impossible to *separate* the mere *tactual feeling,* from the *feeling of length,* as to separate the *whiteness* of a *sphere,* in vision, from that *convexity* of the sphere, which the eye, of itself, would have been for ever incapable of perceiving.

As yet, however, the only dimension of the knowledge, of which we have traced the origin, is mere length; and it must still be explained, how we acquire the knowledge of the other dimensions. If we had had but *one* muscle, it seems to me very doubtful, whether it would have been possible for us, to have associated with touch any other notion than that of mere length. But nature has made provision, for giving us a wider knowledge, in the various muscles, which she has distributed over different parts, so as to enable us to perform motions in various directions at the same instant, and thus to have coexisting series of feelings, each of which series was before considered as involving the notion of length. The infant bends one finger gradually on the palm of his hand; the finger, thus brought down, touches one part of the surface of the palm, producing a certain affection of the organ of touch, and a consequent sensation; and he acquires the notion of a certain length, in the remembered succession of the muscular feelings during the contraction:—he bends another finger; *it,* too, touches a certain part of the surface of the palm, producing a certain feeling of touch, that coexists and combines, in like manner, with the remembrance of a certain succession of muscular feelings. When both fingers move together, the coexistence of the two series of successive feelings, with each of which the mind is familiar, gives the notion of coexisting lengths, which receive a sort of unity, from the proximity in succession of the tactual feelings in the contiguous parts of the palm which they touch,—feelings, which have *before* been found to be proximate, when the palm has been repeatedly pressed along a surface, and the tactual feelings of these parts, which the closing fingers touch at the same moment, were always immediately successive,—as immediately successive, as any of the muscular feelings in the series of contraction. When a body is placed in the infant's hand, and its little fingers are bent by it as before, sometimes *one* finger only is impeded in its progress, sometimes *two,* sometimes *three,*—and he thus adds to the notion of mere length, which would have been the same, whatever number of fingers had been impeded, the notion of a certain number of proximate and coexisting lengths, which is the very notion of breadth; and with these, according as the body is larger or smaller, is combined always the tactual affection produced by the pressure of the body, on more, or fewer, of the interior parts of the palm and fingers, which had before become, of themselves, representative of certain lengths, in the manner described; and the concurrence of these three varieties of length, in the single feeling of resistance, in which they all seem to meet, when an incompressible body is placed within the sphere of the closing fingers,—however rude the notions of concurring dimensions *may* be, or rather *must* be, as at first formed,—seems at least to afford the rude elements, from which, by the frequent repetition of the feeling of resistance, together with the proximate lengths, of which it has become representative, clearer notions of the kind may gradually arise.

The progressive contractions of the various muscles which move the arms, as affording similar successions of feelings, may be considered in precisely the same light, as sources of the knowledge of extension; and, by their motion in various directions, at the same time with the motion of the fingers, they concur powerfully, in modifying, and correcting, the information received from these. The whole hand is brought, by the motion of the arm, to touch one part of the face or body; it is then moved, so as to touch another part, and, with the frequent succession of the simple feelings of touch, in these parts, is associated the feeling of the intervening *length,* derived from the sensations that accompanied the progressive contraction of the arm. But the motion is not always the same; and, as the same feeling of touch, in one part, is thus followed by various feelings of touch in different parts, with various series of muscular feelings between, the notion of length in various *directions,* that is to say, of length in various series commencing from one power, is obtained in another way. That the knowledge of extension, or, in other words, the association of the notion of succession with the simple feelings of touch, will be rude and indistinct at first, I have already admitted; but it will gradually become more and more distinct and precise: as we can have no doubt, that the perception of distance by the eye, is, in the first stages of visual association, very indistinct, and becomes clearer after each repeated trial. For many weeks or months, all is confusion in the visual perceptions, as much as in the *tactual* and *muscular*. Indeed, we have abundant evidence of this continued progress of vision, even in mature life, when, in certain professions that require nice perceptions of distance, the power of perception itself, by the gradual acquisitions which it obtains from experience, seems to unfold itself more and more, in proportion to the wants that require it.

The theory of the notion of extension, of which I have now given you but a slight outline, might, if the short space of these Lectures allowed sufficient room, be developed with many illustrations, which it is now impossible to give to it. I must leave you, in some measure, to supply these for yourselves.

It may be thought, indeed, that the notion of *time*, or *succession*, is, in this instance, a superfluous incumbrance of the theory, and that the same advantage might be obtained, by supposing the muscular feelings themselves, independently of the notion of their succession, to be connected with the notion of particular lengths. But this opinion, it must be remarked, would leave the difficulty *precisely as before*; and sufficient evidence, in confutation of it, may be found in a very simple experiment, which it is in the power of any one to make. The experiment I cannot but consider as of the more value, since it seems to me,—I will not say *decisive*, for that is too presumptuous a word,—but strongly *corroborative* of the theory, which I have ventured to propose; for it shows, that, even after all the acquisitions, which our sense of touch has made, the notion of extension is still modified, in a manner the most striking and irresistible, by the mere change of accustomed *time*. Let any one, with his eyes shut, move his hand, with moderate velocity, along a part of a table, or any other hard smooth surface, the portion, over which he presses, will appear of a certain length; let him move his hand more rapidly, the portion of the surface pressed will appear *less*; let him move his hand *very slowly*, and the length, according to the degree of the slowness, will appear increased, in a most wonderful proportion. In this case, there is precisely the same quantity of muscular contraction, and the same quantity of the organ of touch compressed, whether the motion be rapid, moderate, or slow. The only circumstance of difference is the time, occupied in the succession of the feelings; and this difference is sufficient to give complete diversity to the notion of length.

If any one, with his eyes shut, suffer his hand to be guided by another, *very* slowly along any surface unknown to him, he will find it impossible to form any accurate guess as to its length. But it is not *necessary*, that we should be previously unacquainted with the *extent of surface*, along which the motion is performed; for the illusion will be nearly the same, and the experiment, of course, be still more striking, when the motion is along a surface with which we are perfectly familiar, as a book which we hold in our hand, or a desk at which we are accustomed to sit.

I must request you, *not* to *take for granted* the result which I have now stated, but to repeat for yourselves an experiment, which it is so very easy to make, and which, I cannot but think, is so very important, as to the influence of *mere difference of time*, in our estimation of *longitudinal extent*. It is an experiment, tried, unquestionably, in *most unfavourable circumstances*, when our *tactual feelings, representative* of extension, are so strongly *fixed*, by the long experience of our life; and yet, *even now*, you will find, on moving your hand, *slowly* and *rapidly*, along the *same extent of surface*, though with *precisely the same degree of pressure in both cases*, that it is *as* difficult to conceive the extent, thus *slowly* and *rapidly* traversed, to be the *same*, as it is difficult to conceive the *extent of visual distance* to be *exactly the same*, when you look alternately through the different ends of an *inverted telescope*. If, when all other circumstances are the same, *the different visual feelings*, arising from difference of the mere direction of light, be *representative* of *length*, in the *one* case,—the *longer or shorter succession of time*, when all other circumstances are the same, has surely *as much* reason to be considered as *representative* of it, in the *other* case.

Are we, then, to believe, that the *feeling* of *extension*, or, in other words, of the definite figure of bodies, is a *simple feeling* of touch, *immediate*, *original*, and *independent of time;* or is there not rather reason to think, as I have endeavoured to show, that it is a *compound feeling,* of which *time,* that is to say, our *notion* of succession, is an *original element?*

* * *

Knowledge about spatial localization was considerably accelerated with the invention by Wheatstone of the *stereoscope* and the research it made possible. As described in the passage that follows, Wheatstone was able to show that binocular parallax, or retinal disparity, was a major cue to depth perception, independently of convergence and accommodation.

The stereoscope had great appeal for both the scientist and the general public, the latter through the development of a "hand stereoscope" by Oliver Wendell Holmes and through his writings extolling its artistic and historical virtues.* As a scientific instrument, the stereoscope enabled the presentation of independent stimulation to each eye. The left- and right-eye views could be selected to copy those normally received in binocular vision, or they could be chosen to provide stimulation not encountered under natural viewing conditions.

Stereoscopic presentations that reproduce normal binocular stimulation typically "fuse" and yield stable, three-dimensional percepts. However, when the left- and right-eye stereoscopic images are not "compatible"—when they do not reproduce stimulation that might accompany the natural binocular viewing of an object—for example, when the left eye is presented with a red surface and the right eye with a green one, then an interesting perceptual effect results, commonly referred to as *rivalry.* In the excerpts that follow, Wheatstone describes the stereoscope and his use of it to investigate retinal disparity as a cue to depth, and also, briefly, his discovery of rivalry and some of its determinants. Rivalry receives additional treatment in Chapter 6.

* O. W. Holmes. Sun-painting and sun-sculpture. *Atlantic Monthly,* 1861, 8, 13–29.

Charles Wheatstone

Some Remarkable Phenomena of Binocular Vision

When an object is viewed at so great a distance that the optic axes of both eyes are sensibly parallel when directed towards it, the perspective projections of it, seen by each eye separately, are similar, and the appearance to the two eyes is precisely the same as when the object is seen by one eye only. There is, in such case, no difference between the visual appearance of an object in relief and its perspective projection on a plane surface; and hence pictorial representations of distant objects, when those circumstances which would prevent or disturb the illusion are carefully excluded, may be rendered such perfect resemblances of the objects they are intended to represent as to be mistaken for them; the Diorama is an instance of this. But this similarity no longer exists when the object is placed so near the eyes that to view it the optic axes must converge; under these conditions a different perspective projection of it is seen by each eye, and these perspectives are more dissimilar as the convergence of the optic axes becomes greater. This fact may be easily verified by placing any figure of three dimensions, an outline cube for instance, at a moderate distance before the eyes, and while the head is kept perfectly steady, viewing it with each eye successively while the other is closed. . . . fig. 13. represents the two perspective projections of a cube; *b* is that seen by the right eye, and *a* that presented to the left eye; the figure being supposed to be placed about seven inches immediately before the spectator.

C. Wheatstone, *Contributions to the Physiology of Vision.—Part the First. On some remarkable, and hitherto unobserved, Phenomena of Binocular Vision. Philosophical Transactions*, Royal Society of London, 1838, [128], 371–394. This selection is from pp. 371–377 and 386–387.

The appearances, which are by this simple experiment rendered so obvious, may be easily inferred from the established laws of perspective; for the same object in relief is, when viewed by a different eye, seen from two points of sight at a distance from each other equal to the line joining the two eyes. Yet they seem to have escaped the attention of every philosopher and artist who has treated of the subjects of vision and perspective. I can ascribe this inattention to a phenomenon leading to the important and curious consequences, which will form the subject of the present communication, only to this circumstance; that the results being contrary to a principle which was very generally maintained by optical writers, viz. that objects can be seen single only when their images fall on corresponding points of the two retinae, an hypothesis which will be hereafter discussed, if the consideration ever arose in their minds, it was hastily discarded under the conviction, that if the pictures presented to the two eyes are under certain circumstances dissimilar, their differences must be so small that they need not be taken into account.

It will now be obvious why it is impossible for the artist to give a faithful representation of any near solid object, that is, to produce a painting which shall not be distinguished in the mind from the object itself. When the painting and the object are seen with both eyes, in the case of the painting two *similar* pictures are projected on the retinae, in the case of the solid object the pictures are *dissimilar;* there is therefore an essential difference between the impressions on the organs of sensation in the two cases, and consequently between the perceptions formed in the mind; the painting therefore cannot be confounded with the solid object.

After looking over the works of many authors who might be expected to have made some remarks relating to this subject, I have been able to find but one, which is in the Trattato della Pittura of Leonardo da Vinci. This great artist and ingenious philosopher observes, "that a painting, though conducted with the greatest art and finished to the last perfection, both with regard to its contours, its lights, its shadows and its colours, can never show a relievo equal to that of the natural objects, unless these be viewed at a distance and with a single eye. For," says

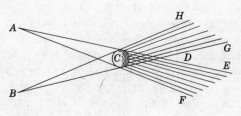

Figure 1

he, "if an object C (. . . fig. 1.) be viewed by a *single* eye at A, all objects in the space behind it, included as it were in a shadow ECF cast by a candle at A, are invisible to the eye at A; but when the other eye at B is opened, part of these objects become visible to it; those only being hid from both eyes that are included, as it were, in the double shadow CD, cast by two lights at A and B, and terminated in D, the angular space EDG beyond D being always visible to both eyes. And the hidden space CD is so much the shorter, as the object C is smaller and nearer to the eyes. Thus the object C seen with both eyes becomes, as it were, transparent, according to the usual definition of a transparent thing; namely, that which hides nothing beyond it. But this cannot happen when an object, whose breadth is bigger than that of the pupil, is viewed by a single eye. The truth of this observation is therefore evident, because a painted figure intercepts all the space behind its apparent place, so as to preclude the eyes from the sight of every part of the imaginary ground behind it."

Had Leonardo da Vinci taken, instead of a sphere, a less simple figure for the purpose of his illustration, a cube for instance, he would not only have observed that the object obscured from each eye a different part of the more distant field of view, but the fact would also perhaps have forced itself upon his attention, that the object itself presented a different appearance to each eye. He failed to do this, and no subsequent writer within my knowledge has supplied the omission; the projection of two obviously dissimilar pictures on the two retinae when a single object is viewed, while the optic axes converge, must therefore be regarded as a new fact in the theory of vision.

It being thus established that the mind perceives an object of three dimensions by means of the two dissimilar pictures projected by it on the two retinae, the following question occurs: What would be the visual effect of simultaneously presenting to each eye, instead of the object itself, its projection on a plane surface as it appears to that eye? To pursue this inquiry it is necessary that means should be contrived to make the two pictures, which must necessarily occupy different places, fall on similar parts of both retinae. Under the ordinary circumstances of vision the object is seen at the concourse of the optic axes, and its images consequently are projected on similar parts of the two retinae; but it is also evident that two exactly similar objects may be made to fall on similar parts of the two retinae, if they are placed one in the direction of each optic axis, at equal distances before or beyond their intersection.

Fig. 2. represents the usual situation of an object at the intersection of the optic axes. In fig. 3. the similar objects are placed in the direction of the optic axes before their intersection, and in fig. 4. beyond it. In all these three cases the mind perceives but a single object, and refers it to the place where the optic axes meet. It will be observed, that when the eyes converge beyond the objects, as in fig. 3., the right hand object is seen by the right eye, and the left hand object by the left eye; while when the axes converge nearer than the objects, the right hand object is seen by the left eye, and conversely. As both of these

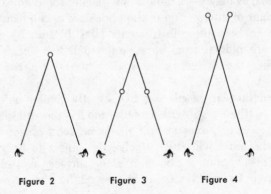

Figure 2   Figure 3   Figure 4

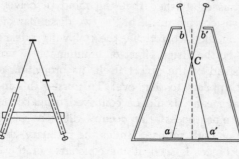

Figure 5   Figure 6

modes of vision are forced and unnatural, eyes unaccustomed to such experiments require some artificial assistance. If the eyes are to converge beyond the objects, this may be afforded by a pair of tubes (fig. 5.) capable of being inclined towards each other at various angles, so as to correspond with the different convergences of the optic axes. If the eyes are to converge at a nearer distance than that at which the objects are placed, a box (fig. 6.) may be conveniently employed; the objects a a' are placed distant from each other, on a stand capable of being moved nearer the eyes if required, and the optic axes being directed towards them will cross at c, the aperture b b' allowing the visual rays from the right hand object to reach the left eye, and those from the left hand object to fall on the right eye; the coincidence of the images may be facilitated by placing the point of a needle at the point of intersection of the optic axes c, and fixing the eyes upon it. In both these instruments (figs. 5. and 6.) the lateral images are hidden from view, and much less difficulty occurs in making the images unite than when the naked eyes are employed.

Now if, instead of placing two exactly similar objects to be viewed by the eyes in either of the modes above described, the two perspective projections of the same solid object be so disposed, the mind will still perceive the object to be single, but instead of a representation on a plane surface, as each drawing appears to be when separately viewed by that eye which is directed towards it, the observer will perceive a figure of three dimensions, the exact counterpart of the object from which the drawings were made. To make this matter clear I will mention one or two of the most simple cases.

If two vertical lines near each other, but at different distances from the spectator, be regarded first with one eye and then with the other, the distance between them when referred to the same plane will appear different; if the left hand line be nearer to the eyes, the distance as seen by the left eye will be less than the distance as seen by the right eye; fig. 7. will render this evident; *a a′* are vertical sections of the two original lines, and *b b′* the plane to which their projections are referred. Now if the two lines be drawn on two pieces of card, at the respective distances at which they appear to each eye, and these cards be afterwards viewed by either of the means above directed, the observer will no longer see two lines on a plane surface, as each card separately shows; but two lines will appear, one nearer to him than the other, precisely as the original vertical lines themselves. Again, if a straight wire be held before the eyes in such a position that one of its ends shall be nearer to the observer than the other is, each eye separately referring it to a plane perpendicular to the common axis, will see a line differently inclined; and then if lines having the same apparent inclinations be drawn on two pieces of card, and be presented to the eyes as before directed, the real position of the original line will be correctly perceived by the mind.

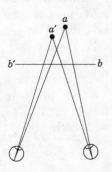

Figure 7

In the same manner the most complex figures of three dimensions may be accurately represented to the mind, by presenting their two perspective projections to the two retinae. But I shall defer these more perfect experiments until I describe an instrument which will enable any person to observe all the phenomena in question with the greatest ease and certainty.

In the instruments above described the optic axes converge to some point in a plane before or beyond that in which the objects to be seen are situated. The adaptation of the eye, which enables us to see distinctly at different distances, and which habitually accompanies every different degree of convergence of the optic axes, does not immediately adjust itself to the new and unusual condition; and to persons not accustomed to experiments of this kind, the pictures will either not readily unite, or will appear dim and confused. Besides this, no object can be viewed according to either mode when the drawings exceed in breadth the distance of the two points of the optic axes in which their centres are placed.

These inconveniences are removed by the instrument I am about to describe; the two pictures (or rather their reflected images) are placed in it at the true concourse of the optic axes, the focal adaptation of the eye preserves its usual adjustment, the appearance of lateral images is entirely avoided, and a large field of view for each eye is obtained. The frequent reference I shall have occasion to make to this instrument, will render it convenient to give it a specific name, I therefore propose that it be called a Stereoscope, to indicate its property of representing solid figures.

The stereoscope is represented by figs. 8. and 9; the former being a front view, and the latter a plan of the instrument. *AA'* are two plane mirrors, about four inches square, inserted in frames, and so adjusted that their backs form an angle of 90° with each other; these mirrors are fixed by their common edge

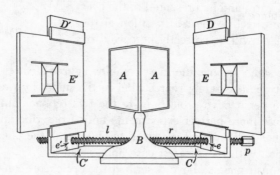

Figure 8

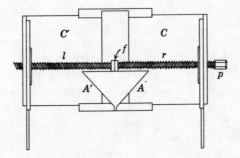

Figure 9

against an upright B, or which was less easy to represent in the drawing, against the middle line of a vertical board, cut away in such manner as to allow the eyes to be placed before the two mirrors. *CC'* are two sliding boards, to which are attached the upright boards *DD'*, which may thus be removed to different distances from the mirrors. In most of the experiments hereafter to be detailed, it is necessary that each upright board shall be at the same distance from the mirror which is opposite to it. To facilitate this double adjustment, I employ a right and a left-handed wooden screw, *r l*; the two ends of this compound screw pass through the nuts *e e'*, which are fixed to the lower parts of the upright boards *DD'*, so that by turning the screw pin *p* one way the two boards will approach, and by turning it the other they will recede from each other, one always preserving the same distance as the other from the middle line *f*. *EE'* are pannels, to which the pictures are fixed in such manner that their corresponding horizontal lines shall be on the same level: these pannels are capable of sliding backwards and forwards in grooves on the upright boards *DD'*. The apparatus having been described, it now remains to explain the manner of using it. The observer must place his eyes as near as possible to the mirrors, the right eye before the right hand mirror, and the left eye before the left hand mirror, and he must move the sliding pannels *EE'* to or from him until the two reflected images coincide at the intersection of the optic axes, and form an image of the same apparent magnitude as each of the component pictures. The pictures will indeed coincide when the sliding pannels are in a variety of different positions, and consequently when viewed under different inclinations of the optic axes; but there is only one position in which the binocular image will be immediately seen single, of its proper magnitude, and without fatigue to the eyes, because in this position only the ordinary relations between the magnitude of the pictures on the retina, the inclination of the optic axes, and the adaptation of the eye to distinct vision at different distances are preserved. The alteration in the apparent magnitude of the binocular images, when these usual relations are disturbed, will be discussed in another paper of this series, with a variety of remarkable phenomena depending thereon. In all the experiments detailed in the present memoir I shall suppose these relations to remain undisturbed, and the optic axes to converge about six or eight inches before the eyes.

If the pictures are all drawn to be seen with the same inclination of the optic axes, the apparatus may be simplified by omitting the screw *r l* and fixing the upright boards *DD'* at the proper distances. The sliding pannels may be dispensed with, and the drawings themselves be made to slide in the grooves.

A few pairs of outline figures, calculated to give rise to the perception of objects of three dimensions when placed in the stereoscope in the manner described, are represented from figs. 10. to 20. They are one half the linear size of the figures actually employed. As the drawings are reversed by reflection in the mirrors, I will suppose these figures to be the reflected images to which the eyes are directed in the apparatus; those marked *b* being seen by the right eye, and those marked *a* by the left eye. The drawings, it has been already explained, are two different projections of the same object seen from two points of sight, the distance between which is equal to the interval between the eyes of the observer; this interval is generally about 2½ inches.

a and *b*, fig. 10. will, when viewed in the stereoscope, present to the mind a line in the vertical plane, with its lower end inclined towards the observer. If the two component lines be caused to turn round their centres equally in opposite directions, the resultant line will, while it appears to assume every degree of in-

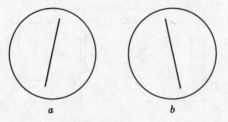

Figure 10

clination to the referent plane, still seem to remain in the same vertical plane.

Fig. 11. A series of points all in the same horizontal plane, but each towards the right hand successively nearer the observer.

Figure 11

Fig. 12. A curved line intersecting the referent plane, and having its convexity towards the observer.

Fig. 13. A cube.

Fig. 14. A cone, having its axis perpendicular to the referent plane, and its vertex towards the observer.

Fig. 15. The frustum of a square pyramid; its axis perpendicular to the referent plane, and its base furthest from the eye.

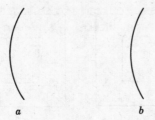

Figure 12

124   Charles Wheatstone

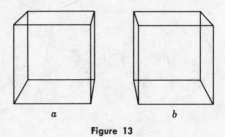

Figure 13

Fig. 16. Two circles at different distances from the eyes, their centres in the same perpendicular, forming the outline of the frustum of a cone.

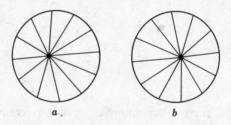

Figure 14

The other figures require no observation.

For the purpose of illustration I have employed only outline figures, for had either shading or colouring been introduced it

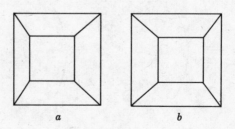

Figure 15

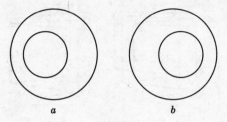

Figure 16

might be supposed that the effect was wholly or in part due to these circumstances, whereas by leaving them out of consideration no room is left to doubt that the entire effect of relief is

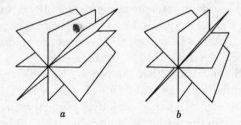

Figure 17

owing to the simultaneous perception of the two monocular projections, one on each retina. But if it be required to obtain the most faithful resemblances of real objects, shadowing and

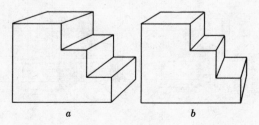

Figure 18

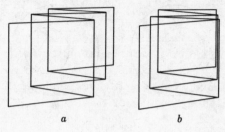

a   *b*

Figure 19

colouring may properly be employed to heighten the effects.
Careful attention would enable an artist to draw and paint the
two component pictures, so as to present to the mind of the observer, in the resultant perception, perfect identity with the object
represented. Flowers, crystals, busts, vases, instruments of various
kinds, &c., might thus be represented so as not to be distinguished
by sight from the real objects themselves.

It is worthy of remark, that the process by which we thus become acquainted with the real forms of solid objects, is precisely
that which is employed in descriptive geometry, an important
science we owe to the genius of Monge, but which is little studied
or known in this country. In this science, the position of a point, a
right line or a curve, and consequently of any figure whatever, is
completely determined by assigning its projections on two fixed
planes, the situations of which are known, and which are not parallel to each other. In the problems of descriptive geometry the

a   *b*

Figure 20

two referent planes are generally assumed to be at right angles to each other, but in binocular vision the inclination of these planes is less according as the angle made at the concourse of the optic axes is less; thus the same solid object is represented to the mind by different pairs of monocular pictures, according as they are placed at a different distance before the eyes, and the perception of these differences (though we seem to be unconscious of them) may assist in suggesting to the mind the distance of the object. The more inclined to each other the referent planes are, with the greater accuracy are the various points of the projections referred to their proper places; and it appears to be a useful provision that the real forms of those objects which are nearest to us are thus more determinately apprehended than those which are more distant.

A very singular effect is produced when the drawing originally intended to be seen by the right eye is placed at the left hand side of the stereoscope, and that designed to be seen by the left eye is placed on its right hand side. A figure of three dimensions, as bold in relief as before, is perceived, but it has a different form from that which is seen when the drawings are in their proper places. There is a certain relation between the proper figure and this, which I shall call its *converse* figure. Those points which are nearest the observer in the proper figure are the most remote from him in the converse figure, and *vice versâ*, so that the figure is, as it were, inverted; but it is not an exact inversion, for the near parts of the converse figure appear smaller, and the remote parts larger than the same parts before the inversion. Hence the drawings which, properly placed, occasion a cube to be perceived, when changed in the manner described, represent the frustum of a square pyramid with its base remote from the eye: the cause of this is easy to understand.

This conversion of relief may be shown by all the pairs of drawings from fig. 10 to 19. In the case of simple figures like these the converse figure is as readily apprehended as the original one, because it is generally a figure of as frequent occurrence; but in the case of a more complicated figure, an architectural design, for instance, the mind, unaccustomed to perceive its converse, because it never occurs in nature, can find no meaning in it. . . .

If we regard a picture with the right eye alone for a considerable length of time it will be constantly perceived; if we look at another and dissimilar picture with the left eye alone its effect will be equally permanent; it might therefore be expected, that if each of these pictures were presented to its corresponding eye at the same time the two would appear permanently superposed on each other. This, however, contrary to expectation, is not the case.

If *a* and *b* (fig. 25.) are each presented at the same time to a different eye, the common border will remain constant, while the letter within it will change alternately from that which would be perceived by the right eye alone to that which would be perceived by the left eye alone. At the moment of change the letter which has just been seen breaks into fragments, while fragments of the letter which is about to appear mingle with

Figure 25

them, and are immediately after replaced by the entire letter. It does not appear to be in the power of the will to determine the appearance of either of the letters, but the duration of the appearance seems to depend on causes which are under our control: thus if the two pictures be equally illuminated, the alternations appear in general of equal duration; but if one picture be more illuminated than the other, that which is less so will be perceived during a shorter time. I have generally made this experiment with the apparatus, fig. 6. When complex pictures are employed in the stereoscope, various parts of them alternate differently.

There are some facts intimately connected with the subject of the present article which have already been frequently observed. I allude to the experiments, first made by Du Tour, in which two different colours are presented to corresponding parts of the two retinae. If a blue disc be presented to the right eye and a yellow disc to the corresponding part of the left eye, instead of a green disc which would appear if these two colours had mingled before their arrival at a single eye, the mind will perceive the two colours distinctly one or the other alternately predominating either partially or wholly over the disc. In the same manner the mind perceives no trace of violet when red is presented to one eye and blue to the other, nor any vestige of orange when red and yellow are separately presented in a similar manner. These experiments may be conveniently repeated by placing the coloured discs in the stereoscope, but they have been most usually made by looking at a white object through differently coloured glasses, one applied to each eye.

In some authors we find it stated, contrary to fact, that if similar objects of different colour be presented one to each eye, the appearance will be that compounded of the two colours. Dr. Reid and Janin are among the writers who have fallen into this inconsiderate error, which arose no doubt from their deciding according to previous notions, instead of ascertaining by experiment what actually does happen....

* * *

To show that retinal disparity is a major cue to depth perception is not to understand fully how the cue is utilized—that is, how the information implicit in the disparity between the two images is encoded, transmitted centrally in the nervous system, and decoded to yield a three-dimensional percept. This kind of question raises many types of issues, some metaphysical (for example, how does nervous activity eventuate in what we call percepts?) and some neurophysiological (for example, how are the electrical impulses generated by stimulation of points in the two retinas combined centrally to yield a given perceptual effect, that is, fusion and the consequent experience of depth when the two retinal images are compatible and suppression and rivalry when the images are incompatible?)

Issues of the latter sort might be pursued, for example, by investigating the functional organization of each retinal surface and the way, if any, in which that retinal organization is centrally represented. It turns out that research directed at this problem has revealed a point-for-point representation of the retina on the visual cortex. Thus, just as each sense modality has a locus of termination in the brain, so too do the individual receptor elements within the eye itself.

Further, if each sense modality can be identified by its terminus in the brain, so too can each retinal receptor. In short, it seems that each point in the retina transmits a message to the brain, which "tags" its point of origin. Finally, and most conveniently, the central organization of termination points preserves the spatial organization of retinal points. There can be, then, a one-to-one correspondence between a pattern of retinal stimulation and a pattern of brain activity. To tie the pattern of brain activity to an external visual object that is spatially localized, it remains only to relate the retinal pattern to the stimulating object.

The eye, of course, moves, as does the head and also the entire body. Any fixed object will therefore be projected onto the same area of the retina, and hence the same cortical area, only when the eye is in a given position relative to the object. As the eye moves relative to a fixed object, the retinal area stimulated by that object will vary. But this variation is *systematically* related to the amount and direction of movement. In short, an external object can be localized, via the position on the retina of its projected image, only if the position and orientation of the eye can be "taken into account."

The above rather complicated, but still quite partial, treatment is meant as an introduction to the following passage by Lotze. The main purpose of this passage is to show how objects might be localized in space. Lotze does this by way of his famous "theory of local signs," which is his alternative to the type of "tagging" mechanism suggested in the above discussion.

By local signs, the relative positions of retinal points can be appreciated. This, however, does not suffice for location of the stimulating object in space, and for solution of this problem Lotze turns to eye- and body-movement and feedback therefrom. In a passage not quoted here Lotze generalizes his argument to account for the perception of depth.

Hermann Lotze

The Intuitions of Space

Metaphysic raises the doubt, whether space is actually extended and we, together with 'Things,' are contained in it; whether—just the reverse—the whole spatial world is not rather only a form of intuition in us.

This question we for the present leave one side, and in the meantime take our point of departure from the assumption, previously alluded to, with which we are all conversant. But since Things in space can never become the object of our perception by virtue of their bare existence, and, on the contrary, become such solely through the effects which they exercise upon us, the question arises: How do the Things by their influence upon us bring it to pass, that we are compelled mentally to represent them in the same reciprocal position in space, in which they actually exist outside of us?

In the case of the eye, nature has devised a painstaking structure, such that the rays of light which come from a luminous point are collected again at one point on the retina, and that the different points of the image, which originate here, assume

H. Lotze. Outlines of psychology. Dictated portions of the lectures of Hermann Lotze. Translated and edited from the 3rd German edition (1884) by G. T. Ladd. Boston: Ginn, 1886. The first German edition of Grundzüge der Psychologie was published in Leipzig by Hirzel in 1881. This selection is drawn from Chapter IV of the Ladd translation.

the same reciprocal relation toward one another as the points of the object outside of us, to which they correspond. Without doubt, this so-called 'image of the object,' so carefully prepared, is an indispensable condition of our being able mentally to present the object in its true form and position. But it is the source of all the errors in this matter, to believe that the bare existence of this image, without anything else, explains our idea of the position of its parts. The entire image is essentially nothing but a representative of the external object, transposed into the interior of the organ of sense; and how we know and experience aught of it, is now just as much the question as the question previously was,—How can we perceive the external object?

If one wished to conceive of the soul itself as an extended being, then the impressions on the retina would, of course, be able to transplant themselves, with all their geometrical regularity, to the soul. One point of the soul would be excited as green, the other red, a third yellow; and these three would lie at the corners of a triangle precisely in the same way as the three corresponding excitations on the retina.

It is also obvious, however, that there is no real gain in all this. The bare fact that three different points of the soul are excited is, primarily, a disconnected three-fold fact. A knowledge thereof, however, and therefore a knowledge of this three-foldness, and of the reciprocal positions of the three points, is, nevertheless, by no means given in this way: but such knowledge could be brought about only by means of a uniting and relating activity; and this itself, like every activity, would be perfectly foreign to all predicates of extension and magnitudes in space.

The same thought is more immediately obvious if we surrender this useless notion of the soul being extended, and consider it as a supersensible essence, which, in case we wish to bring it at all into connection with spatial determinations, could be represented only as an indivisible point.

On making the transition into this indivisible point, the manifold impressions must obviously lose all the geometrical relations which they might still have upon the extended retina,—just in the same way as the rays of light, which converge at the single focus of a lens, are not side by side with one another, but only all

together, in this point. Beyond the focus, the rays diverge in the
same order as that in which they entered it. Nothing analogous
to this, however, happens in our consciousness; that is to say,
the many impressions, which were previously side by side with
one another, do not actually again separate from each other;
but, instead of this, the aforesaid activity of mental presentation
simply occurs, and it transposes their images to different places
in the space that is only 'intuited' by it.

Here, too, the previous observation holds good: The mental
presentation *is* not that which it presents; and the idea of a point
on the left does not lie on the left of the idea of a point on the
right; but of one mental presentation, which in itself has no spatial properties whatever, both points are merely themselves so
presented before the mind, as though one lay to the left, the
other to the right.

The following result now stands before us: Many impressions
exist conjointly in the soul, although not spatially side by side
with one another; but they are merely together in the same way
as the synchronous tones of a chord; that is to say, qualitatively
different, but not side by side with, above or below, one another.
Notwithstanding, the mental presentation of a spatial order must
be produced again from these impressions. The question is, therefore, in the first place, to be raised: How in general does the
soul come to apprehend these impressions, not in the form in
which they actually are,—to wit, non-spatial,—but as they are not,
in a spatial juxtaposition?

The satisfactory reason obviously cannot lie in the impressions
themselves, but must lie solely in the nature of the soul in which
they appear, and upon which they themselves act simply as
stimuli.

On this account, it is customary to ascribe to the soul this
tendency to form an intuition of space, as an originally inborn
capacity. And indeed we are compelled to rest satisfied with this.
All the 'deductions' of space, hitherto attempted, which have
tried to show on what ground it is necessary to the nature of the
soul to develop this intuition of space, have utterly failed of
success. Nor is there any reason to complain over this matter;
for the simplest modes of the experience of the soul must always

merely be recognized as given facts,—just as, for example, no one seriously asks why we only hear, and do not rather taste, the waves of air.

The second question is much more important. Let it be assumed that the soul once for all lies under the necessity of mentally presenting a certain manifold as in juxtaposition in space; How does it come to localize every individual impression at a definite place in the space intuited by it, in such manner that the entire image thus intuited is similar to the external object which acted on the eye?

Obviously, such a clue must lie in the impressions themselves. The simple quality of the sensation 'green' or 'red' does not, however, contain it; for every such color can in turn appear at every point in space, and on this account does not, of itself, require always to be referred to the one definite point.

We now remind ourselves, however, that the carefulness with which the regular position on the retina of the particular excitations is secured, cannot be without a purpose. To be sure, an impression is not *seen* at a definite point on account of its *being situated* at such point; but it may perhaps by means of this definite situation *act* on the soul otherwise than if it were elsewhere situated.

Accordingly we conceive of this in the following way: Every impression of color r—for example, red—produces on all places of the retina, which it reaches, the same sensation of redness. In addition to this, however, it produces on each of these different places, a, b, c, a certain accessory impression, α, β, γ, which is independent of the nature of the color seen, and dependent merely on the nature of the place excited. This second local impression would therefore be associated with every impression of color r, in such manner that rα signifies a red that acts on the point a, rβ signifies the same red in case it acts on the point b. These associated accessory impressions would, accordingly, render for the soul the clue, by following which it transposes the same red, now to one, now to another spot, or simultaneously to different spots in the space intuited by it.

In order, however, that this may take place in a methodical way, these accessory impressions must be completely different from the main impressions, the colors, and must not disturb the latter. They must be, however, not merely of the same kind among themselves, but wholly definite members of a series or a system of series; so that for every impression r there may be assigned, by the aid of this adjoined 'local sign,' not merely a particular, but a quite definite spot among all the rest of the impressions.

The foregoing is the theory of 'Local Signs.' Their fundamental thought consists in this, that all spatial differences and relations among the impressions on the retina must be compensated for by corresponding non-spatial and merely intensive relations among the impressions which exist together without space-form in the soul; and that from them in reverse order there must arise, not a new actual arrangement of these impressions in extension, but only the mental presentation of such an arrangement in us. To such an extent do we hold this principle to be a necessary one.

On the contrary, only hypotheses are possible in order to answer the question, In what do those accessory impressions requisite consist, so far as the sense of sight is concerned? We propose the following conjecture:—

In case a bright light falls upon a lateral part of the retina, on which—as is well known—the sensitiveness to impressions is more obtuse than in the middle of the retina, then there follows a rotation of the eye until the most sensitive middle part of the retina, as the receptive organ, is brought beneath this light: we are accustomed to style this the "fixation of vision" upon the aforesaid light. Such motion happens involuntarily, without any original cognition of its purpose, and uniformly without cognition of the means by which it is brought about. We may therefore reckon it among the so-called reflex motions, which originate by means of an excitation of one nerve, that serves at other times for sensation, being transplanted to motor nerves without any further assistance from the soul and in accordance with the pre-existing anatomical connections; and these latter nerves being therefore stimulated to execute a definite motion in a perfectly mechanical way. Now in order to execute such a rotation of the eye as serves the purpose previously alluded to, every single spot in the retina, in case it is stimulated, must occasion a magnitude and direction of the aforesaid rotation peculiar to it alone. But at the same time all these rotations of the eye would be perfectly comparable motions, and, of course, members of a system of series that are graded according to magnitude and direction.

The application of the foregoing hypothesis (many more minute particular questions being disregarded) we conceive of as follows:—In case a bright light falls upon a lateral point **P** of a retina, which has not yet had any sensation of light whatever, then there arises, in consequence of the connection in the excitation of the nerves, such a rotation of the eye as that, instead of the place **P**, the place **E** of clearest vision is brought beneath the approaching stimulus of the light. Now while the eye is passing through the arc **PE**, the soul receives at each instant a feeling of its momentary position,—a feeling of the same kind as that by which we are, when in the dark, informed of the position of our limbs. To the arc **PE** there corresponds then a series of constantly changing feelings of position, the first member of which we call π, and the last of which we call ϵ.

If now, in a second instance, the place **P** is again stimulated by the light, then there originates not simply the rotation **PE** for a second time, but the initial member of the series of feelings of position, π, reproduces in memory the entire series associated with it, $\pi\epsilon$; and this series of mental presentations is independent of the fact that at the same time also the rotation of the eye **PE** actually follows.

Exactly the same thing would hold good of another point **R**; only the arc **RE**, the series of feelings $\rho\epsilon$, and also the initial member of the series, ρ, would have other values.

Now finally, in case it came about that both places, **P** and **R**, were simultaneously stimulated with an equal intensity, and that the arcs **PE** and **RE** were equal but in opposite directions to each other, then the actual rotation of the eye **PE** and **RE** could not take place; on the other hand, the excitation upon the places **P** and **R** is nevertheless not without effect; each reproduces the series of feelings of position belonging to it,—respectively, $\pi\epsilon$ and $\rho\epsilon$. Although therefore the eye does not now move, yet there is connected with every excitation of the places **P** and **R** the mental presentation of the magnitude and of the qualitative peculiarity of a series of changes, which consciousness or the common feeling would have to experience, in order that these excitations may fall upon the place of clearest vision, or, according to the customary expression, in the line of vision.

And now we assert that to see anything 'to the right' or 'to the left' of this line of vision means nothing more than this, to be conscious of the magnitude of the achievement which would be necessary to bring the object into this line.

By the foregoing considerations nothing further would be established than the relative position of the single colored points in the field of vision. The entire image, on the contrary, would still have no place at all in a yet larger space; indeed, even the mental presentation of such a place would as yet have no existence.

Now this image first attains a place with reference to the eye, the repeated opening and closing of which, since it can become known to us in another way, is the condition of its existence or non-existence. That is to say, the visible world is *in front* before our eyes. What is behind us not merely has no existence whatever for us, but we do not once know that there is anything which should be called 'behind.'

The motions of the body lead us further. If the field of vision in a position of rest contains from left to right the images a b c, and we then turn ourselves to the right upon our axis, a vanishes, but d appears on the right, and therefore the images b c d, c d e, d e f, . . . x y z, y z a, z a b, a b c, succeed in order. As a result of such recurrence of the images with which we began, the two following thoughts originate; namely, that the visible world of objects exists in a closed circuit of extension about us, and that the alteration of our own position, which we perceive by means of the changing feelings of position while turning, depends upon an alteration of our relation to this immovable world of objects,—that is to say, upon a *motion*.

It is easily understood that the mental picture of a spherical extension originates from the aforesaid mental picture of a closed horizon by means of repeatedly turning in a similar way in various other directions.

But, nevertheless, this spherical surface also would always have only a superficial extension; no intimation would as yet exist of a *depth* to space.

Now the mental presentation, to the effect that something like a third dimension of space in general exists, cannot originate of itself, but only through the experience which we have in case we move about among the visible objects. From the manifold displacements which the particular visual images experience, in a manner that is tedious to describe but very easy to imagine, we gain the impression, that each line in an image originally seen is the beginning of new surfaces which do not coincide with that previously seen, but which lead out into this space, now extended on all sides, to greater or less distances from the line.

Another question to be treated subsequently is this: By what means do we estimate the different magnitudes of the distance into this depth of space?

The crossing of the rays of light in the narrow opening of the pupil is the cause of the image of the upper points of the object being formed beneath, that of the lower points above on the retina; and of the whole picture having therefore a position the reverse of the object. But it is a prejudice on this account to consider seeing in inverse position to be natural, and seeing in upright position to be mysterious. Like every geometrical property of the image, so this one of its position, too, on passing into consciousness, is completely lost; and the position in which we see things is in no way prejudiced by the aforesaid position of the image on the retina.

Now, however, in order that we may be able to ascribe to objects a position at all, in order therefore that the expressions 'above,' 'below,' 'upright,' and 'inverted,' may have a meaning, we must have, independent of all sensation by sight, a mental picture of a space in which the entire content of the field of vision shall be arranged, and in which 'above' and 'below' are two qualitatively opposite and, on this account, not exchangeable directions.

The muscular feeling affords us such a mental presentation. 'Below' is the place toward which the direction of gravity moves;

'above,' the opposite. Both directions are distinguished perfectly for us by means of an immediate feeling; and, on this account, we are never deceived even in the dark about the position and situation of our body.

Accordingly we see objects 'upright' in case the lower points of the object are reached by one and the same movement of the eyes simultaneously with those points of our own body which are 'below' according to the testimony of the aforesaid muscular feeling; and the upper points by a movement which, according to the same testimony, renders visible simultaneously the upper parts of our own selves.

Now it is exactly such agreement that is secured in *our* eye, in which the axis lies in front of the sensitive retina, by means of the inverted position of the retinal image. In an other eye, in which the sensitive surface should be placed in front of the axis, and yet the greatest sensitiveness also should appear in the middle portion of that surface, the retinal image would have to stand upright to serve the same purpose.

The final and valid answer to the question, why we have single vision with two eyes, is not to be given. As is well known, it does not always happen. The rather must two impressions fall on two quite definite points of the retina in order to coalesce. We see double, on the contrary, if they fall on other points. Naturally, we shall say: The two places which belong together would have to impart like local signs to their impressions, and thereby render them indistinguishable; but we are not able to demonstrate in what manner this postulate is fulfilled. Physiology, too, in the last analysis, satisfies itself with a mere term for the fact; it calls 'identical' those places in both retinas which give one simple impression, and 'non-identical' those which give a double impression.

Irritations of the skin we naturally refer at once to the place of the skin on which we see them acting. But in case of their repetition, when we are not able to see them, we have no assistance from remembering them; for the most ordinary stimuli have already in the course of our life touched all possible places of the skin, and could therefore now as well be referred to one place as to another. In order that they may be correctly localized, they would have at every instant to tell us anew where they belong; that is to say, there must be attached to the main impression (impact, pressure, heat or cold) an auxiliary impression which is independent of the latter and, on the contrary, dependent on the place of the skin that is irritated.

The skin can supply such local signs; for since it is connected without interruption, a single point of it cannot be irritated at all, without the surrounding portion experiencing a displacement, pulling, stretching, or concussion of some kind. But, further, since the skin possesses at different places a different thickness, different tension or liability to displacement,—extends sometimes above the firm surfaces of the bones, sometimes over the flesh of the muscles, sometimes over cavities; since, moreover, the members being manifold, these relations change from one stretch of skin to another; therefore the aforesaid sum of secondary effects around the point irritated will be different for each one from the remainder; and such effects, if they are taken up by the nerve-endings and act on consciousness, may occasion the feelings so difficult to describe, according to which we distinguish a contact at once place from the same contact at another.

It cannot be said, however, that each point of the skin has its special local sign. It is known from the investigations of E. H. Weber, that on the margin of the lips, the tip of the tongue, the tips of the fingers, being touched in two places (by the points of a pair of compasses) can be distinguished as two at an interval of only ½ line; while there are places on the arms, legs, and on the back, which require for making the distinction a distance between them of as much as 20 lines. We interpret this in the following way. Where the structure of the skin changes little for long stretches, the local signs also alter only a little from point to point. And if two stimuli act simultaneously, and accordingly a reciprocal disturbance of these secondary effects occurs, they will be undistinguishable; on the contrary, in cases where both stimuli act successively, and therefore the aforesaid disturbance ceases, both are still frequently distinguishable. On the other hand, we know nothing further to allege as to how the extraordinary sensitiveness—for example—of the lips is occasioned.

The preceding statement merely explains the possibility of distinguishing impressions made at different places; but each impression must also be referred to the definite place at which it acts.

This is easy for one who sees, since he already possesses a picture of the surfaces of his own body; and, on this account, he now by means of the unchanging local sign, even in the dark, translates each stimulus which he has once seen act on a definite place, to the same place in this picture of the body that is mentally presented before him. One born blind would be compelled to construct such a picture first by means of the sense of touch; and this naturally is accomplished through motions of the tactual members and by estimating the distances which they would have to travel in order to reach from contact at the point **a** to contact at the other point **b**. It is to be considered, however, that these motions—which in this case are not seen—are perceivable only by so-called muscular feelings;—that is to say, by feelings which in themselves are merely certain species of the way *we feel*, and do not of themselves at all indicate the motions which are in fact the causes of them.

Now it cannot be described, how it is that this interpretation of the muscular feelings actually originates in the case of those born blind; but the helps which lead to it are very probably found in the fact, that the sense of touch as well as the eye can receive many impressions simultaneously, and that, in case of a movement, the previous impression does not vanish without trace and have its place taken by a wholly new one; but that, in the manner previously alleged, the combinations **a b c, b c d**, etc., follow one another, and therefore some part in common is always left over for the next two impressions. By this alone does it seem possible to awaken the idea that the same occurrence, from which the series of changeable muscular feelings originates for us, consists in an alteration of our relation to a series of objects previously existent side by side and to be found arranged in a definite order; it consists, therefore, in a *motion*.

It is questionable whether the mental picture of space which one born blind attains solely by the sense of touch will be altogether like that of one who sees; it is rather to be assumed that a much less intuitable system of mental presentations of time, of the magnitude of motion, and of the exertion which is needed in order to reach from contact at one point to that at another, takes the place of the clear, easy, and at once all-comprehending intuition, with which he who sees is endowed.

* * *

From the point of view of a person who is simultaneously viewing an object and the image cast by that object on the retina of another person, the retinal image is "upside-down" or *inverted*. The inversion is a simple result of the optical characteristics of the eye; it has fascinated many serious perceptual theorists, who have wondered why we do not see the world upside-down in agreement with the image on the retina rather than rightside-up in agreement with the external physical world. To others,—including Lotze, who discusses this issue above, in the course of the presentation of his theory of local signs—retinal inversion poses no more of a problem than would an uninverted retinal image; to treat inversion as a special problem is to deal with a pseudo-problem.

Pseudo-problems are not entirely evil, however, for they sometimes motivate research that otherwise would not have been done and thereby generate information of value independently of its relation to the original problem, or pseudo-problem. One such line of research was motivated by a concern over retinal inversion. It began with the pioneering work of Stratton, a portion of which is presented below. The main purpose of Stratton's research is to trace the phenomenal, and behavioral, changes, if any, that accompany prolonged stimulation by retinal images that are not inverted. Stratton's method and some of his findings are described in the following excerpt.

George Malcolm Stratton

Vision Without Inversion of the Retinal Image

In the November [1896] number of this *Review,* I gave a short account of some preliminary experiments on vision without inversion of the retinal image. Brief as the experiments were, they gave certain definite results and hinted at others which would probably be obtained if the artificial conditions were continued for a longer time. The course of the experience also showed that problems much wider than that of upright vision were involved, and that a careful record of a longer test might throw light on these also. I was strengthened in this view that the experiment bore on other problems at least as important as that of upright vision, by the remarks of Professor Titchener when the paper was publicly read; while the questions of Professor Münsterberg, on the same occasion, suggested the need of more careful observations in regard to dizziness and the localization of sounds.

The earlier paper was thus necessarily vague or silent on a number of questions in regard to which a more careful and extended experiment could hardly fail to produce something of interest—on such questions as, for instance, whether the reconstruction of the directions, right and left, proceeded exactly parallel to that of the directions up and down; what the connection of visual and tactual localization really is, which enables the one to influence the other; and, finally, what were the more definite conditions under which the harmonious accommodation to the abnormal sight-perceptions waxed and waned. It was also necessary that a nicer distinction should constantly be observed between acts or ideas arising as a result of deliberate volition

G. M. Stratton. Vision without inversion of the retinal image. *Psychol. Rev.,* 1897, **4**, 341–381. pp. 341–346; 466–471; 480–481.

and those which arose effortless and unpremeditated. In other words, the account should clearly distinguish at any given stage of the experiment between processes which occurred spontaneously and those which could be called up only by force of will.

The present experiment was conducted under almost the same conditions as those of the preliminary experiment. I myself was again the observer, and the apparatus was the one described in the earlier article, except that a thin cloth-lined plaster cast of the region about the eyes was substituted for the padded paste-board case which before had held the tube of lenses. In making the cast a small mass of non-adhesive material was placed directly over each eye, and afterwards removed from the cast; so that during the experiment the inner lining of the case did not press on the eyes, nor interfere in the least with their free movement. In front of the right eye there was an opening in the cast, into which the tube of four lenses before described fitted exactly. This tube was carefully focussed and set at such a distance from the eye as to give a clear visual field of about 45° compass. The cast could then be bound to the head by a set of tapes, and although somewhat heavier than the paste-board case, was nevertheless much more comfortable, because it pressed evenly over a large surface of the face. By this device all light was excluded, except such as came through the lenses into the right eye.

The time was not spent, as before, entirely indoors. Besides the free range of the house, I could walk in a secluded garden; and since the experiment fell at a time of bright moonlight, I took, every evening but the first, a long walk through the village, accompanied and, when there was need, guided by a companion. The experiment lasted, this time, from noon of the first day until noon of the eighth day—a net period in all (after subtracting the time during which the eyes were blindfolded), of about 87 hours, as against 21½ for the previous experiment. The actual record for the eight days is shown in the table on the opposite page.

At all times when the glasses were not worn, the eyes were thoroughly blindfolded. Careful notes were made every day, to record as exactly as possible the actual state of the experience at that time.

Day	Hour of Putting Glasses on	Hour of Taking Glasses off	Length of Time Glasses were Worn
1st	12 m.	9 p. m.	9 hrs.
2d	9 a. m.	9 p. m.	12 hrs.
3d	9 a. m.	9 p. m.	12 hrs.
4th	9 a. m.	9:45 p. m.	12 hrs., 45 mins.
5th	9:50 a. m.	10:30 p. m.	12 hrs., 40 mins.
6th	9:50 a. m.	9:45 p. m.	11 hrs., 55 mins.
7th	9:15 a. m.	9:45 p. m.	12 hrs., 30 mins.
8th	8 a. m.	12:10 p. m.	4 hrs., 10 mins.

Total, 87 hrs.

Before I attempt a narrative of the experience under the experimental conditions, a word or two as to the terminology will be necessary. One has constantly to make a distinction between the appearance of an object as seen through the reversing lenses, and either the appearance it had before the lenses were put on, or the appearance it would have had if the lenses were removed and normal vision restored. This appearance just described is called in the narrative the 'older,' the 'normal,' often the 'pre-experimental' appearance of the object; while the appearance through the lenses is called its 'newer' or 'later' appearance. Similar distinguishing terms have also to be used with reference to the mere representation or idea of an object, as contrasted with its actual perception.

It is perhaps unnecessary to state that the accommodation to the artificial conditions was, in my case, probably more rapid than it would have been, had I not retained some of the effects of the practice gained in the earlier experiment, about five months before.

The experience from day to day was as follows:

First Day.—The entire scene appeared upside down. When I moved my head or body so that my sight swept over the scene, the movement was not felt to be solely in the observer, as in normal vision, but was referred both to the observer and to objects beyond. The visual picture seemed to move through the field of view faster than the accompanying movement of my body, although in the same direction. It did not feel as if I were visually ranging over a set of motionless objects, but the whole field of things swept and swung before my eyes.

Almost all movements performed under the direct guidance of sight were laborious and embarrassed. Inappropriate movements were constantly made; for instance, in order to move my hand from a place in the visual field to some other place which I had selected, the muscular contraction which would have accomplished this if the normal visual arrangement had existed, now carried my hand to an entirely different place. The movement was then checked, started off in another direction, and finally, by a series of approximations and corrections, brought to the chosen point. At table the simplest acts of serving myself had to be cautiously worked out. The wrong hand was constantly used to seize anything that lay to one side. In pouring some milk into a glass, I must by careful trial and correction bring the surface of the milk to the spout of the pitcher, and then see to it that the surface of the milk in the glass remained everywhere equally distant from the glass's rim.

The unusual strain of attention in these cases, and the difficulty of finally getting a movement to its goal, made all but the simplest movements extremely fatiguing. The observer was thus tempted to omit all those which require nice guidance, or which included a series of changes or of rapid adaptations to untried visual circumstances. Relief was sometimes sought by shutting out of consideration the actual visual data, and by depending solely on tactual or motor perception and on the older visual representations suggested by these. But for the most part this tendency was resisted, and movements were performed with full attention to what was visually before me. Even then, I was frequently aware that the opposite, the merely represented, arrangement was serving as a secondary guide along with the actual sight perceptions, and that now the one factor and now the other came to the foreground and was put in control. In order to write my notes, the formation of the letters and words had to be left to automatic muscular sequence, using sight only as a guide to the general position and direction on my paper. When hesitation occurred in my writing, as it often did, there was no resort but to picture the next stroke or two in pre-experimental terms, and when the movement was once under way, control it visually as little as possible.

The scene before me was often reconstructed in the form it would have had in normal vision; and yet this translation was not carried to such an extent as at the beginning of the first experiment. The scene was now accepted more as it was immediately presented. Objects of sight had more reality in them—had more the character of 'things,' and less that of phantasms—than when the earlier trial began. Objects were, however, taken more or less isolatedly; so that inappropriateness of place with reference to other objects even in the same visual field was often, in the general upheaval of the experience, passed by unnoticed. I sat for some time watching a blazing open fire, without seeing that one of the logs had rolled far out on the hearth and was filling the room with smoke. Not until I caught the odor of the smoke, and cast about for the cause, did I notice what had occurred.

Similarly, the actual visual field was, for the most part, taken by itself and not supplemented, as in normal vision, by a system of objects gathered and held from the preceding visual experience. Sporadic cases occurred, in which some object out of sight was represented as it had just been seen; but in general all things not actually in view returned to their older arrangement and were represented, if at all, as in normal sight. Usually this was the case also in picturing an unseen movement of some part of my body. At times, however, both the normal and the later representation of the moving part spontaneously arose in the mind, like an object and its mirrored reflection. But such cases occurred only when actual sight had just before revivified the later memory-image.

As regards the parts of the body, their pre-experimental representation often invaded the region directly in sight. Arms and legs in full view were given a double position. Beside the position and relation in which they were actually seen, there was always in the mental background, in intimate connection, with muscular and tactual sensations, the older represention of these parts. As soon as my eyes were closed or directed elsewhere, this older representation gathered strength and was the dominant image. But other objects did not usually have this double localization while I looked at them, unless non-visual sensations came from the objects. Touch, temperature, or sounds, brought up a visual image of the source in pre-experimental form.

Anticipations of contact from bodies seen to be approaching, arose as if particular places and directions in the visual field had the same meaning as in normal experience. When one side of my body approached an object in view, the actual feeling of contact came from the side opposite to that from which I had expected it. And likewise in passing under a hanging lamp, the lamp, in moving toward what in normal experience had been the lower part of the visible field, produced a distinct anticipatory shrinking in the region of the chin and neck, although the light really hung several inches above the top of my head.

Whether as a result of the embarrassment under which nearly all visually guided movements were performed, or as a consequence of the swinging of the scene, described above, there were signs of nervous disturbance, of which perhaps the most marked was a feeling of depression in the upper abdominal region, akin to mild nausea. This disappeared, however, toward evening; so that by half-past seven it was no longer perceptible. . . .

Eighth day.—Before putting the glasses on, representations of the older sort held sway.

During the morning, after the glasses were in place, I noticed that as far as the unseen portions of my body were concerned, the relation of right and left was, for the most part, a reproduction of the older visual right and left; that is to say, a contact on the right side of the body at some point beyond the reach of sight was felt and visually represented on the (old) visual right side. Occasionally the opposite visual side was suggested, but the sensations were rarely indeed felt there. The case was quite different as regards the seen parts of my body, although even here uncertainly and sudden alteration of reference occurred. The illusion of contact on the opposite hand to the one actually touched, arose as on the two preceding days. I often hesitated which hand was the appropriate one for grasping some object in view, began the movement with the wrong hand and then corrected the mistake. If I was attentive to the new visual representation of some part of my body which was about to be touched, and expected the contact there, the contact was felt in the new position and no change of reference occurred. Immediately afterwards there usually arose a sort of tactual after-image on the other visual side. When the original contact was unexpected, the visual image and the tactual localization might simultaneously be both old and new, or might be old alone, with perhaps a merely visual image in the new direction, although without any real reference of the touch-sensations to this image.

Localization of sounds varied, being different when the source of sound was in sight from what it was when this was out of sight, and also in the latter case differing with different directions of attention, or with different suggestions as to the direction from which the sound came. The fire, for instance, sputtered where I saw it. The tapping of my pencil on the arm of my chair seemed without question to issue from the visible pencil. Even when I tapped on the wall to one side, out of sight, if in making the stroke I invariably passed my hand and pencil before my eyes and in the direction of the unseen part of the wall, and attempted to picture the contact in harmony with this movement, I actually heard the sound come from the new visual direction, although not with full and unequivocal localization. There was a strong temptation to localize the sound on the other side also. And this rival localization rose into full life the instant I ceased to keep before me the image of the pencil striking on the new visual side.

The influence of the suggestion coming from recent and repeated movements before the eyes was likewise apparent in localizing parts of my body which could not be brought into the visual field. Thus the involuntary inattentive localization of my forehead and hair was the old localization lasting from pre-experimental sight. But a series of visible movements of my hand to my hair, together with fixed attention on the goal of these movements, made the sensations of touch temporarily come, without difficulty, from this new direction. Sensations of contact on the lips, however, were not so readily dislodged from their old position. In eating at table, the movements of my hands and of pieces of food across the visual field, constantly suggested that my mouth must lie between the line of sight and the new position of my legs. But the actual contact on my lips instantly dispelled this suggestion and located my mouth definitely and indubitably on the other side of the line of sight. The place of the actual contact and that of the merely suggested contact were thus in striking contrast. But when I did my best to visualize my lips in the direction of the suggested contact and strained my attention in this direction, the actual contact did not dissipate this image or carry it to the old position of my mouth, but the touch-sensations seemed to come from the new direction. Without such a willful visualization and strain of attention the actual contact always reversed the involuntary suggestion coming from the visible movements toward the new position of my mouth. Even when my forehead and hair temporarily seemed to lie on the (new) upper side of the line of sight, this did not prevent my mouth from being felt on the *same* side. But the new localization of forehead and scalp undoubtedly had a tendency to drive the mouth out of its old localization; for I found that less effort of attention and visualization was required to make the tactual sensations of the lips come from the new position, when the top of the head had already been carried over to its new position. No doubt there was a disturbing incongruity in having both my mouth and the top of my head on the same side of the line of sight; consequently the re-localization of one tended to carry the other to the opposite side of the visual line.

In other cases the re-localization of bodily parts that were beyond the reach of sight was brought about by the suggestive influence of such movements as I have just described, without any voluntary attention or visualization of the parts whatever. As I rocked in my chair, I found that by throwing my arms up through the field of sight into the visual region in which my shoulders, according to the old experience, were wont to be localized, the repeated feeling of the unimpeded motion of my hands through this region destroyed the old representation of my shoulders and back, and gave them a localization in harmony with the new visual experience, except that (as I noticed) my head seemed too deep-set in my shoulders—in fact, seemed buried in them almost up to my ears.

The harmonization of the new experience and the suppression or subordination of insistent remnants of the old were always apparent during active operations in the visual surroundings, as has been described for several of the preceding days. While I sat passively the old localization of unseen parts of my body often came back, or perhaps was the usual form in which they appeared. But the instant I began to rock my chair the new position of these parts came prominently forward, and, except in the case of my shoulders and back, readily felt more real than the old. And in walking, when hands and feet rhythmically made their appearance in the visual field, the old representation, except perhaps for some faint inharmonious sensations in the back, was fully expelled without employing any device of will or of attention whatever. The attempt to represent my body in its older form or position ended in a faint, lifeless outline, deficient, as far as I could make out, in those parts which (in a different direction, of course) were actually in sight. The sight of these parts made it impossible to represent them in harmony with the older experience. If in walking I allowed my feet to remain outside the field of view and they relapsed into their older localization, they returned, although still unseen, to their new position as soon as I approached a step or other slight obstacle on the floor.

As long as the new localization of my body was vivid, the general experience was harmonious, and everything was right side up. But when, for any of the reasons already given—an involuntary lapse into the older memory-materials, or a willful recall of these older forms—the pre-experimental localization of my body was prominently in mind, then as I looked out on the scene before me the scene was involuntarily taken as the standard of right directions, and my body was felt to be in an inharmonious position with reference to the rest. I seemed to be viewing the scene from an inverted body.

When the time came for removing the glasses at the close of the experiment, I thought it best to preserve as nearly as possible the size of visual field to which I had now grown accustomed; so that any results observed might be clearly due solely to the reversion of my visual objects and not to a sudden widening of the visual field. Instead, therefore, of removing the plaster cast from my face, I closed my eyes and had an assistant slip out the brass tube which held the lenses, and insert in its place an empty black-lined paper tube that gave about the same range of vision. On opening my eyes, the scene had a strange familiarity. The visual arrangement was immediately recognized as the old one of pre-experimental days; yet the reversal of everything from the order to which I had grown accustomed during the past week, gave the scene a surprising, bewildering air which lasted for several hours. It was hardly the feeling, though, that things were upside down.

When I turned my body or my head, objects seemed to sweep before me as if they themselves were suddenly in motion. The 'swinging of the scene,' observed so continuously during the first days of the experiment, had thus returned with great vividness. It rapidly lost this force, however, so that at the end of an hour the motion was decidedly less marked. But it was noticeable the rest of the day, and in a slight degree even the next morning.

Movements which would have been appropriate to the visual arrangement during the experiment, were now repeatedly performed after this arrangement had been reversed. In walking toward some obstacle on the floor of the room—a chair, for instance—I turned the wrong way in trying to avoid it; so that I frequently either ran into things in the very effort to go around them, or else hesitated, for the moment, bewildered what I should do. I found myself more than once at a loss which hand I ought to use to grasp the door-handle at my side. And of two doors, side by side, leading to different rooms, I was on the point of opening the wrong one, when a difference in the metal work of the locks made me aware of my mistake. On approaching the stairs, I stepped up when I was nearly a foot too far away. And in writing my notes at this time, I continually made the wrong movement of my head in attempting to keep the centre of my visual field somewhere near the point where I was writing. I moved my head upward when it should have gone downward; I moved it to the left when it should have gone to the right. And this to such a degree as to be a serious disturbance. While walking, there were distinct signs of vertigo and also the depression in the upper abdominal region, noticed during the earlier days of the experiment. The feeling that the floor and other visual objects were swaying, in addition to the symptoms just mentioned, made my walking seem giddy and uncontrollable. No distinct errors in localizing parts of my body occurred; I was more than once surprised, however, to see my hands enter the visual field from the old lower side.

Objects in the room, at a distance of ten or twelve feet from me, seemed to have lost their old levels and to be much higher than they were either during the experiment or before the experiment. The floor no longer seemed level, but appeared to slope up and away from me, at an angle of perhaps five degrees. The windows and other prominent objects seemed also too high. This strange aspect of things lasted (as did also the swinging of the scene, the feeling of giddiness, and certain inappropriate movements) after the plaster cast had been removed and the normal compass of the visual field was restored. In the dim light of the next morning, the upward slope of the floor and the unusual position of the windows were distinctly noticeable.

It is clear, from the foregoing narrative, that our total system of visual objects is a comparatively stable structure, not to be set aside or transformed by some few experiences which do not accord with its general plan of arrangement. It might perhaps have been supposed beforehand that if one's visual perceptions were changed, as in the present experiment, the visual ideas of things would without resistance conform to the new visual experiences. The results show, however, that the harmony comes only after a tedious course of adjustment to the new conditions, and that the visual system has to be built anew, growing from an isolated group of perceptions. The older visual representations for the most part have to be suppressed rather than reformed. . . .

But to return to the more significant features of the experiment. These are, without doubt, found in the results bearing on the relation between touch and sight, and through them on the interrelation of the senses generally. The experiment makes it clear that the harmony between sight and touch does not depend on the inversion of the retinal image. The spatial identity of tactual and visual objects evidently does not require that there should be a visual transposition of objects or that they should be given some special direction in the visual field. The chief reason for the existence of the projection theory is therefore taken away. Nor, on the other hand, are the visual directions made known to us and determined through our perceiving the 'absolute,' or pure motor, direction of the movements which alter the line of sight. The facts all go to show that the direction of movements of the head or eyes is not judged on purely muscular evidence, independently of the simultaneous changes in vision itself. On the contrary the movements are soon felt as having a direction opposite to that of the objects passing through the visual field. During the experiment, for instance, I often felt my eyes turn toward the sky and away from my feet, although they really turned toward my feet. The felt direction of the movement is therefore relative to the direction of the movement of visual objects, and the 'absolute' muscular direction cuts no decisive figure in the perception at all. This will no doubt seem a hard saying to those who have been pinning their faith more and more on the unimpeachable witness of muscular sensations. It certainly makes the eye-movement doctrine of visual directions of little practical assistance for understanding the harmony between sight and touch.

This harmony, as was said, seems rather to be an accord of the *ideas* suggested in terms of one of the senses, with the *perceptions* of the same sense. When touch and sight agree, it means that the perceptions of sight are spatially identical with the visual suggestions produced by touch, and that the preceptions of touch spatially identical with the tactual suggestions produced by sight. The doctrine of a correspondence of local signs, stated some pages back, makes it easy to see how such a harmony could grow up; and, at the same time, how a reharmonization of touch . . . and sight is possible, whatever may be the position of the retinal image. The view makes provision, therefore, for the special results of the experiment, as well as for the normal course of our experience; which the current doctrines concerning the interplay of touch and sight seem hardly able to do.

5

Perceptual Integration
and Unconscious Processes

One of the distinguishing features of nineteenth century psychology was its *elementarism,* the analysis of experience into its simplest components. This analytic approach worked, and still works, exceedingly well in the other sciences (for example, witness the spectacular accomplishments of atomic physics). In particular, as was indicated in Chapter 2 of this volume, the research of Bell and Magendie and the other great nineteenth century physiologists and anatomists had considerable impact as a model for an elementaristic approach in psychology. Indeed, philosophy—physiology's mate in the genesis of modern psychology—already had set the stage for this approach to psychology in the seventeenth and eighteenth centuries, especially through the influence of the physician-turned-philosopher, John Locke, and others of the British school.

Locke's goal was to uncover the source and validity of human knowledge; that is, Locke was an epistemologist. Having rejected those earlier views (for example, of Plato, Descartes, and others), which held man to be innately endowed with certain basic concepts or ideas, Locke proposed that the mind, at birth, was a blank tablet (*tabula rasa*); the source of all ideas must then ultimately be sensory experience, discounting revelation as a potential source.

As a part of his argument, Locke hypothesized two types of sensory experience (or "ideas," as Locke called them). One type

155

of idea, such as solidity, extension, movement, reflected primary qualities of objects; the other type, such as color, taste, sound, did not. Ideas of this latter sort arose out of the interaction between primary qualities of objects and the perceiving organism. This distinction between primary and secondary qualities of objects is one that was easily invalidated (see, for example, Berkeley's *A Treatise Concerning the Principles of Human Knowledge*).

A second distinction made by Locke remained a part of psychology much longer than did his distinction between primary and secondary qualities. This was his distinction between simple and complex ideas. The sensory experience, "red," is a simple idea, while the idea, "apple," is a complex one, comprised of such simple ideas as red, round, sweet, firm, and so on. The complex idea, in short, is a collection of simple ideas, the collection having been formed through the co-existence of simple ideas in some man's mind. The principle of the formation of complex ideas is a simple principle of association—those ideas which happen to co-exist will coalesce to form a complex idea. Fortunately, although the process of association is entirely mechanical, and therefore subject to the most absurd whims of chance, the typical complex idea corresponds to the nature of some real, physical object. Of course, one might create for oneself complex ideas (unicorns, Shangri-La) with no referent in reality just by recombining simple ideas in novel ways. Thus, complex ideas can originate in either of two ways: passively, through the individual's experience with real objects; or, actively, through analysis of complex ideas of the first sort into their simple elements and regrouping of these elements into hitherto unexperienced combinations.

In his epistemological explorations Locke goes well beyond this stage, but for the present purpose this is the place to stop in describing his work. Translate ideation into perception, and the essence of the nineteenth century approach to perception is manifest. Certain experiences are simple, elementary (call them sensations?), and certain experiences are complex (call them perceptions?), the complex experiences having developed, through the principle of association, out of simple, elementary experiences. One task for scientific psychology is, then, to uncover the basic, elementary sensations and their attributes via analysis of complex perceptions. Having accomplished this first task, that is, having found the elements, the psychologist must then tackle the second major task, which is to show how the elements combine to form the complex perceptions that real people experience.

Just as it is much easier for the novice to take a watch apart than it is to put the pieces back together again in working order, so the task of analyzing perception into its elements was much easier than the task of explaining their synthesis. The main barrier to this enterprise was the failure of elements to appear in ordinary experience. Perceptual phenomena that theoretically should be complex were experienced as simple, whole, unified, and immediate. If this were a mystery story (which, in a way, it is) it might be called *The Case of the Missing Elements*.

Of course, the missing elements constituted a problem only for those who expected to find them: synthesis is a task only for those who begin with analysis. It happens that the first three theorists represented in this chapter, John Stuart Mill, Helmholtz, and Wundt, all share the same basic elementaristic-associationistic approach. They all agree that perception issues from combinations of simple, sensory elements (and memory traces thereof), the combinations having been formed through the fortuitous association of these elements in the individual's experience. Starting from this common premise, Mill, Helmholtz, and Wundt treat the problem of synthesis in somewhat different ways, though the similarities among them are much more evident than their differences.

Mill's approach stems directly from the one offered by James Mill, his father and tutor, in the latter's *Analysis of the Phenomena of the Human Mind*. In the following passage J. S. Mill criticizes the work of Sir William Hamilton and justifies his criticism by elaborating the "principle of obliviscence." According to this principle, which might be said to do little more than restate the original problem, not all the elements that generate a percept need appear in consciousness; what does appear is only what the individual attends to, or is interested in. What interests the perceiver, in turn, is usually the end-product or focal point

158   John Stuart Mill

of what might be a long chain, or complex network, of associated elements. Ordinary perceptual experience, therefore, would rarely include the elements of which it is constructed. Their absence from consciousness, however, does not negate their genetic significance.

The following excerpt from the work of J. S. Mill should suffice to illustrate both his own approach and that of his father, James. But two sentences from James Mill are well worth quoting here, lest he suffer complete obliviscence from J. S. Mill; lest the antecedent ideas of the father be forgotten and all attention be absorbed by the words of his son.

It not unfrequently happens in our associated feelings, that the antecedent is of no importance farther than it introduces the consequent. In these cases, the consequent absorbs all the attention, and the antecedent is instantly forgotten.*

John Stuart Mill

A Law of Obliviscence

. . . I have already made mention of a very important part of the Laws of Association, which may be termed the Laws of Obliviscence. If Sir W. Hamilton had sufficiently attended to these laws he never could have maintained, that if we knew the parts before the whole, we must continue to know the parts better than the whole. It is one of the principal Laws of Obliviscence, that when a number of ideas suggest one another by association with such certainty and rapidity as to coalesce together in a group, all those members of the group which remain

J. S. Mill. *An examination of Sir William Hamilton's philosophy* (6th ed.). London: Longmans, Green, & Co., 1889, pp. 323–326. First edition published in 1865.

* J. Mill. *Analysis of the phenomena of the human mind.* In two volumes. London: Baldwin and Cradock, 1829, Vol. I. p. 76.

long without being specially attended to, have a tendency to
drop out of consciousness. Our consciousness of them becomes
more and more faint and evanescent, until no effort of attention
can recall it into distinctness, or at last recall it at all. Any one
who observes his own mental operations will find this fact exemplified in every day of his life. Now the law of attention is
admitted to be, that we attend only to that which, either on its
own or on some other account, interests us. In consequence,
what interests us only momentarily we only attend to momentarily; and do nòt go on attending to it, when that, for the sake
of which alone it interested us, has been attained. Sir W. Hamilton would have found these several laws clearly set forth, and
abundantly exemplified, in the work of Mr. Mill which he had
before him. It is there shown how large a proportion of all our
states of feeling pass off without having been attended to, and
in many cases so habitually that we become. finally incapable
of attending to them. This subject was also extremely well understood by Reid, who, little as he had reflected on the principle
of Association, was much better acquainted with the laws of
Obliviscence than his more recent followers, and has excellently
illustrated and exemplified some of them. Among those which
he has illustrated the most successfully, one is, that the very
great number of our states of feeling which, being themselves
neither painful nor pleasurable, are important to us only as signs
of something else, and which by repetition have come to do
their work as signs with a rapidity which to our feelings is instantaneous, cease altogether to be attended to; and through that
inattention our consciousness of them either ceases altogether, or
becomes so fleeting and indistinct as to leave no reliable trace
in the memory. This happens, even when the impressions which
serve the purpose of signs are not mere ideas, or reminiscences,
of sensation, but actual sensations. After reading a chapter of
a book, when we lay down the volume do we remember to have
been individually conscious of the printed letters and syllables
which have passed before us? Could we recall, by any effort of
mind, the visible aspect presented by them, unless some unusual
circumstance has fixed our attention upon it during the perusal?
Yet each of these letters and syllables must have been present

to us as a sensation for at least a passing moment, or the sense could not have been conveyed to us. But the sense being the only thing in which we are interested—or, in exceptional cases, the sense and a few of the words or sentences—we retain no impression of the separate letters and syllables. This instance is the more instructive, inasmuch as, the whole process taking place within our means of observation, we know that our knowledge begins with the parts, and not with the whole. We know that we perceived and distinguished letters and syllables before we learnt to understand words and sentences; and the perceptions could not, at that time, have passed unattended to; on the contrary, the effort of attention of which those letters and syllables must have been the object, was probably, while it lasted, equal in intensity to any which we have been called upon to exercise in after life. Were Sir W. Hamilton's argument valid, one of two things would follow. Either we have even now when we read in a book, a more vivid consciousness of the letters and syllables than of the words and sentences (and by parity of reason a more vivid consciousness of the words and sentences than of the general purport of the discourse): or else, we could read sentences off hand at first, and only by subsequent analysis discovered the letters and syllables. If ever there was a *reductio ad absurdum*, this is one.

The facts on which Sir W. Hamilton's argument rests, are obviously accounted for by the laws which he ignores. In our perceptions of objects, it is generally the wholes, and the wholes alone, that interest us. In his example, that of a friend's countenance, it is (special motives apart) only the friend himself that we are interested about; we care about the features only as signs that it is our friend whom we see, and not another person. Unless therefore the face commands our attention by its beauty or strangeness, or unless we stamp the features on our memory by acts of attention directed upon them separately, they pass before us and do their work as signs, with so little consciousness that no distinct trace may be left in the memory. We forget the details even of objects which we see every day, if we have no motive for attending to the parts as distinguished from the wholes, and have cultivated the habit of doing so. That this is consistent with having known the parts earlier than the wholes, is proved not only by the case of reading, but by that of playing on a musical instrument, and a hundred other familiar instances; by everything, in fact, which we learn to do. When the wholes alone are interesting to us, we soon forget our knowledge of the component parts, unless we purely keep it alive by conscious comparison and analysis. . . .

* * *

The central assumption in the Mills' argument is that one perceptual event, especially the last one in a rapid sequence, can wipe out or obliterate from consciousness other, typically antecedent, events. This seems a very unlikely assumption, for once an event has occurred, and made an impact, how can it be eliminated by subsequent events? But unlikely as the assumption might seem, something very much like it does indeed turn out empirically to be true, as revealed in research by Baxt, Pieron, Werner, Kolers and Rosner, Sperling, Lindsley and Emmons and others on a phenomenon now referred to as "backward masking" or "metacontrast."* For example, a visual stimulus, presented for a very brief duration (but long enough to be correctly identified under control conditions) will simply not be seen if followed by a surrounding stimulus, when the latter is sufficiently intense and occurs within about 50 milliseconds of the former. There is even some evidence, admittedly controversial, that such a masked stimulus, even though undetected, can influence behavior.†

The Mills' account of perception also seems unlikely on the grounds that the associationistic process they describe ought to consume time, whereas the perception of objects or patterns

---

* For a review of this literature, see D. H. Raab. Backward masking. *Psychol. Bull.*, 1963, **60**, 118–129.
† See, for example, P. A. Kolers Subliminal stimulation in problem-solving. *Amer. J. Psychol.*, 1957, **70**, 437–441.

appears to be instantaneous. But even this objection seems controverted by recent evidence that shows complex percepts to develop over time.*

The experiments alluded to above, of course, do not "prove" the Mills' position, nor were they designed with that intent. They do, however, make the associationist account more tenable than it would at first appear.

Helmholtz, in the following excerpt, presents another answer to the problem of perceptual integration and the effect on it of previous experience. His arguments are better grounded in fact than the versions of the Mills or Locke and perhaps more convincingly offered, but essentially Helmholtz's is the same empiricist-associationist approach as that of his less experimentally oriented predecessors.

There is one terminological difference that should be noted. Helmholtz explicitly uses the term, "unconscious," in his reference to "unconscious conclusions," through the mediation of which ambiguous sensations are translated into definite, usually veridical, but sometimes illusory, percepts. By "unconscious" Helmholtz means nothing more than that the processes so designated occur without the awareness of the individual. In this respect Helmholtz's use of the term is not novel. It had been employed previously in a similar vein by Leibnitz and others.† A more dynamic connotation of the term "unconscious" emerged with the development of Freud's psychoanalytic theory. Some of this dynamic flavor can be found in the fourth excerpt in this chapter, which is taken from Binet.

* G. Smith Visual perception: An event over time. *Psychol. Rev.*, 1957, 64, 306–313.
† L. L. Whyte *The unconscious before Freud*, New York: Basic Books, 1960.

Hermann Ludwig von Helmholtz

Unconscious Conclusions

. . . The general rule determining the ideas of vision that are formed whenever an impression is made on the eye, with or without the aid of optical instruments, is that *such objects are always imagined as being present in the field of vision as would have to be there in order to produce the same impression on the nervous mechanism, the eyes being used under ordinary normal conditions.* To employ an illustration which has been mentioned before, suppose that the eyeball is mechanically stimulated at the outer corner of the eye. Then we imagine that we see an appearance of light in front of us somewhere in the direction of the bridge of the nose. Under ordinary conditions of vision, when our eyes are stimulated by light coming from outside, if the region of the retina in the outer corner of the eye is to be stimulated, the light actually has to enter the eye from the direction of the bridge of the nose. Thus, in accordance with the above rule, in a case of this kind we substitute a luminous object at the place mentioned in the field of view, although as a matter of fact the mechanical stimulus does not act on the eye from in front of the field of view nor from the nasal side of the eye, but, on the contrary, is exerted on the outer surface of the eyeball and more from behind. The general validity of the above rule will be shown by many other instances that will appear in the following pages.

In the statement of this rule mention is made of the ordinary conditions of vision, when the visual organ is stimulated by light from outside; this outside light, coming from the opaque objects

H. v. Helmholtz. *Helmholtz's treatise on physiological optics.* Vol. III, pp. 2–6 and 11–13. See page 70 for full citation.

in its path that were the last to be encountered, and having reached the eye along rectilinear paths through an uninterrupted layer of air. This is what is meant here by the normal use of the organ of vision, and the justification for using this term is that this mode of stimulation occurs in such an enormous majority of cases that all other instances where the paths of the rays of light are altered by reflections or refractions, or in which the stimulations are not produced by external light, may be regarded as rare exceptions. This is because the retina in the fundus of the firm eyeball is almost completely protected from the actions of all other stimuli and is not easily accessible to anything but external light. When a person is in the habit of using an optical instrument and has become accustomed to it, for example, if he is used to wearing spectacles, to a certain extent he learns to interpret the visual images under these changed conditions.

Incidentally, the rule given above corresponds to a general characteristic of all sense-perceptions, and not simply to the sense of sight alone. For example, the stimulation of the tactile nerves in the enormous majority of cases is the result of influences that affect the terminal extensions of these nerves in the surface of the skin. It is only under exceptional circumstances that the nerve-stems can be stimulated by more powerful agencies. In accordance with the above rule, therefore, all stimulations of cutaneous nerves, even when they affect the stem or the nerve-centre itself, are perceived as occurring in the corresponding peripheral surface of the skin. The most remarkable and astonishing cases of illusions of this sort are those in which the peripheral area of this particular portion of the skin is actually no longer in existence, as, for example, in case of a person whose leg has been amputated. For a long time after the operation the patient frequently imagines he has vivid sensations in the foot that has been severed. He feels exactly the places that ache on one toe or the other. Of course, in a case of this sort the stimulation can affect only what is left of the stem of the nerve whose fibres formerly terminated in the amputated toes. Usually, it is the end of the nerve in the scar that is stimulated by external pressure or by contraction of the scar tissue. Sometimes at night the sensations in the missing extremity get to be so vivid that the patient has to feel the place to be sure that his limb is actually gone.

Thus it happens, that when the modes of stimulation of the organs of sense are unusual, incorrect ideas of objects are apt to be formed; which used to be described, therefore, as *illusions of the senses*. Obviously, in these cases there is nothing wrong with the activity of the organ of sense and its corresponding nervous mechanism which produces the illusion. Both of them have to act according to the laws that govern their activity once for all. It is rather simply an illusion in the judgment of the material presented to the senses, resulting in a false idea of it.

The psychic activities that lead us to infer that there in front of us at a certain place there is a certain object of a certain character, are generally not conscious activities, but unconscious ones. In their result they are equivalent to a *conclusion*, to the extent that the observed action on our senses enables us to form an idea as to the possible cause of this action; although, as a matter of fact, it is invariably simply the nervous stimulations that are perceived directly, that is, the actions, but never the external objects themselves. But what seems to differentiate them from a conclusion, in the ordinary sense of that word, is that a conclusion is an act of conscious thought. An astronomer, for example, comes to real conscious conclusions of this sort, when he computes the positions of the stars in space, their distances, etc., from the perspective images he has had of them at various times and as they are seen from different parts of the orbit of the earth. His conclusions are based on a conscious knowledge of the laws of optics. In the ordinary acts of vision this knowledge of optics is lacking. Still it may be permissible to speak of the psychic acts of ordinary perception as *unconscious conclusions*, thereby making a distinction of some sort between them and the common so-called conscious conclusions. And while it is true that there has been, and probably always will be, a measure of doubt as to the similarity of the psychic activity in the two cases, there can be no doubt as to the similarity between the results of such unconscious conclusions and those of conscious conclusions.

These unconscious conclusions derived from sensation are equivalent in their consequences to the so-called *conclusions from analogy*. Inasmuch as in an overwhelming majority of cases, whenever the parts of the retina in the outer corner of the eye are stimulated, it has been found to be due to external light coming into the eye from the direction of the bridge of the nose, the inference we make is that it is so in every new case whenever this part of the retina is stimulated; just as we assert that every single individual now living will die, because all previous experience has shown that all men who were formerly alive have died.

But, moreover, just because they are not free acts of conscious thought, these unconscious conclusions from analogy are irresistible, and the effect of them cannot be overcome by a better understanding of real relations. It may be ever so clear how we get an idea of a luminous phenomenon in the field of vision when pressure is exerted on the eye; and yet we cannot get rid of the conviction that this appearance of light is actually there at the given place in the visual field; and we cannot seem to comprehend that there is a luminous phenomenon at the place where the retina is stimulated. It is the same way in case of all the images that we see in optical instruments.

On the other hand, there are numerous illustrations of fixed and inevitable associations of ideas due to frequent repetition, even when they have no natural connection, but are dependent merely on some conventional arrangement, as, for example, the connection between the written letters of a word and its sound and meaning. Still to many physiologists and psychologists the connection between the sensation and the conception of the object usually appears to be so rigid and obligatory that they are not much disposed to admit that, to a considerable extent at least, it depends on acquired experience, that is, on psychic activity. On the contrary, they have endeavoured to find some mechanical mode of origin for this connection through the agency of imaginary organic structures. With regard to this question, all those experiences are of much significance which show how the judgment of the senses may be modified by experience and by training derived under various circumstances, and may be adapted to the new conditions. Thus, persons may learn in some measure to utilize details of the sensation which otherwise would escape notice and not contribute to obtaining any idea of the object. On the other hand, too, this new habit may acquire such a hold that when the individual in question is back again in the old original normal state, he may be liable to illusions of the senses.

Facts like these show the widespread influence that experience, training and habit have on our perceptions. But how far their influence really does extend, it would perhaps be impossible to say precisely at present. Little enough is definitely known about infants and very young animals, and the interpretation of such observations as have been made on them is extremely doubtful. Besides, no one can say that infants are entirely without experience and practice in tactile sensations and bodily movements. Accordingly, the rule given above has been stated in a form which does not anticipate the decision of this question. It merely expresses what the result is. And so it can be accepted even by those who have entirely different opinions as to the way ideas originate concerning objects in the external world. . . .

A person in a familiar room which is brightly lighted by the sun gets an apperception that is abundantly accompanied by very vivid sensations. In the same room in the evening twilight he will not be able to recognize any objects except the brighter ones, especially the windows. But whatever he does actually recognize will be so intermingled with his recollections of the furniture that he can still move about in the room with safety and locate articles he is trying to find, even when they are only dimly visible. These images would be utterly insufficient to enable him to recognize the objects without some previous acquaintance with them. Finally, he may be in the same room in complete darkness, and still be able to find his way about in it without making mistakes, by virtue of the visual impressions formerly obtained. Thus, by continually reducing the material that appeals to the senses, the perceptual-image (*Anschauungsbild*) can ultimately be traced back to the pure memory-image (*Vorstellungsbild*) and may gradually pass into it. In proportion as there is less and less material appeal to the senses, a person's movements will, of course, become more and more uncertain, and his apperception less and less accurate. Still there will be no peculiar abrupt transition, but sensation and memory will continually supplement each other, only in varying degrees.

But even when we look around a room of this sort flooded with sunshine, a little reflection shows us that under these conditions too a large part of our perceptual-image may be due to factors of memory and experience. The fact that we are accustomed to the perspective distortions of pictures of parallelopipeds and to the form of the shadows they cast has much to do with the estimation of the shape and dimensions of the room, as will be seen hereafter. Looking at the room with one eye shut, we think we see it just as distinctly and definitely as with both eyes. And yet we should get exactly the same view in case every point in the room were shifted arbitrarily to a different distance from the eye, provided they all remained on the same lines of sight.

Thus in a case like this we are really considering an extremely multiplex phenomenon of sense; but still we ascribe a perfectly definite explanation to it, and it is by no means easy to realize that the monocular image of such a familiar object necessarily means a much more meagre perception than would be obtained with both eyes. Thus too it is often hard to tell whether or not untrained observers inspecting stereoscopic views really notice the peculiar illusion produced by the instrument.

We see, therefore, how in a case of this kind reminiscences of previous experiences act in conjunction with present sensations to produce a perceptual image (*Anschauungsbild*) which imposes itself on our faculty of perception with overwhelming power, without our being conscious of how much of it is due to memory and how much to present perception.

Still more remarkable is the influence of the comprehension of the sensations in certain cases, especially with dim illumination, in which a visual impression may be misunderstood at first, by not knowing how to attribute the correct depth-dimensions; as when a distant light, for example, is taken for a near one, or *vice versa*. Suddenly it dawns on us what it is, and immediately, under the influence of the correct comprehension, the correct perceptual image also is developed in its full intensity. Then we are unable to revert to the previous imperfect apperception.

This is very common especially with complicated stereoscopic drawings of forms of crystals and other objects which come out in perfect clearness of perception the moment we once succeed in getting the correct impression.

Similar experiences have happened to everybody, proving that the elements in the sense-perceptions that are derived from experience are just as powerful as those that are derived from present sensations. All observers who have thoroughly investigated the theory of the sense-perceptions, even those who were disposed to allow experience as little scope as possible, have always admitted this.

Hence, at all events it must be conceded that, even in what appears to the adult as being direct apperception of the senses, possibly a number of single factors may be involved which are really the product of experience; although at the time it is difficult to draw the line between them.

Now in my opinion we are justified by our previous experiences in stating that no indubitable present sensation can be abolished and overcome by an act of the intellect; and no matter how clearly we recognize that it has been produced in some anomalous way, still the illusion does not disappear by comprehending the process. The attention may be diverted from sensations, particularly if they are feeble and habitual; but in noting those relations in the external world, that are associated with these sensations, we are obliged to observe the sensations themselves. Thus we may be unmindful of the temperature-sensation of our skin when it is not very keen, or of the contact-sensations produced by our clothing, as long as we are occupied with entirely different matters. But just as soon as we stop to think whether it is warm or cold, we are not in the position to convert the feeling of warmth into that of coldness; maybe because we know that it is due to strenuous exertion and not to the temperature of the surrounding air. In the same way the apparition of light when pressure is exerted on the eyeball cannot be made to vanish simply by comprehending better the nature of the process, supposing the attention is directed to the field of vision and not, say, to the ear or the skin.

On the other hand, it may also be that we are not in the position to isolate an impression of sensation, because it involves the composite sense-symbol of an external object. However, in this case the correct comprehension of the object shows that the sensation in question has been perceived and used by the consciousness.

My conclusion is, that *nothing in our sense-perceptions can be recognized as sensation which can be overcome in the perceptual image and converted into its opposite by factors that are demonstrably due to experience.*

Whatever, therefore, can be overcome by factors of experience, we must consider as being itself the product of experience and training. By observing this rule, we shall find that it is merely the qualities of the sensation that are to be considered as real, pure sensation; the great majority of space-apperceptions, however, being the product of experience and training.

Still it does not follow that apperceptions, which persist in spite of our better conscious insight and continue as illusions, might not be due to experience and training. Our knowledge of the changes of colour produced in distant objects by the haziness of the atmosphere, of perspective distortions, and of shadow is undoubtedly a matter of experience. And yet in a good landscape picture we shall get the perfect visual impression of the distance and the solid form of the buildings in it, in spite of knowing that it is all depicted on canvas. . . .

* * *

With a firmer basis in experimental data, but with essentially the same approach as Helmholtz and the British philosophers, Wundt also faced the problem of accounting for the integration apparent in unanalyzed perception. Wundt, of course, was the champion of the empiricist-associationist tradition among experimental psychologists, transforming this tradition into a self-conscious scientific system, later to be called Structuralism, and a program for a lifetime of research.

From his research Wundt was able to generate several principles of mental functioning. The one most pertinent to the present chapter is his *Principle of Creative Synthesis,* which is briefly discussed in the following passage. Wundt was led to this principle by a conviction, based on his experiments, that complex perceptual phenomena could not be reconstituted out of an additive combination of elements. If the elements really were there, their synthesis would yield more than what would be expected from a simple summative process. Instead, their synthesis generated an entirely new, *emergent* phenomenon; the process of synthesis, therefore, was not merely combinatorial, but rather it was *creative.*

In the passage quoted, Wundt is careful to point out that creative synthesis does not violate any of the laws of physics, in particular the new, but sacrosanct, law of the conservation of energy, in the development of which, incidentally, Helmholtz had played an important role. This concern about the law of the conservation of energy was vital to Wundt, since his philosophical position on the mind-body problem, psychophysical parallelism, demanded a close correspondence, though not an interaction, between psychological and physico-physiological processes.

Wilhelm Max Wundt

Creative Synthesis

. . . The *principle of psychical resultants* finds its expression in the fact that every psychical compound shows attributes which may indeed be understood from the attributes of its elements after these elements have once been presented, but which are by no means to be looked upon as the mere sum of the attributes of these elements. A compound clang is more in its ideational and

W. Wundt, *Outlines of Psychology.* New York: G. E. Stechert & Co., 1907, pp. 368–370. Third rev. English ed., trans. by C. H. Judd from 7th revised German edition of Wundt's *Grundriss der Psychologie,* Leipzig: Engelmann, 1905. First ed., 1896.

affective attributes than merely a sum of single tones. In spatial and temporal ideas the spatial and temporal arrangement is conditioned, to be sure, in a perfectly regular way by the combination of elements which make up the idea, but the arrangement itself can by no means be regarded as a property of the sensation elements themselves. The nativistic theories which assume this, implicate themselves in contradictions which cannot be solved; and besides, in so far as they admit subsequent changes in the original space perceptions and time perceptions, they are ultimately driven to the assumption of the rise, to some extent at least, of new attributes. Finally, in the apperceptive functions and in the activities of imagination and understanding, this principle finds expression in a clearly recognized form. Not only do the elements united by apperceptive synthesis gain, in the aggregate idea which results from their combination, a new significance which they did not have in their isolated state, but what is of still greater importance, the aggregate idea itself is a new psychical content made possible, to be sure, by the elements, but by no means contained in these elements. This appears most strikingly in the more complex productions of apperceptive synthesis, as for example in a work of art or a train of logical thought.

In psychical resultants there is thus expressed a principle which we may designate, in view of its results, as the *principle of creative synthesis*. This principle has long been recognized in the case of higher mental creations, but it has not been generally applied to the other psychical processes. In fact, through an unjustifiable confusion with the principles of physical causality, it has even been completely reversed. A similar confusion is responsible for the notion that there is a contradiction between the principle of creative synthesis in the mental world and the general principles of natural causation, especially the principle of the conservation of energy. Such a contradiction is impossible from the outset because the points of view of judgment, and therefore of measurements wherever such are made, are different in the two cases, and must be different, since natural science and psychology deal, not with different contents of experience, but with one and the same experience viewed from different sides. Physical measurements have to do with *objective masses, forces, and energies*. These are supplementary concepts which we are obliged to use in judging objective experience; and their general laws, derived as they are from experience, must not be contradicted by any single case of experience. Psychical measurements, which are concerned with the comparison of psychical components and their resultants, have to do with *subjective values and ends*. The subjective value of the psychical combination may be greater than the value of its components, its purpose may be different and higher than theirs, without any change in the masses, forces, and energies concerned. The muscular movements of an external volitional act, the physical processes which accompany sense perception, association, and apperception, all follow invariably the principle of the conservation of energy. But the mental values and ends which these energies represent may be very different in quantity even while the quantity of these energies remains the same.

* * *

Wundt found it necessary to invoke the principle of creative synthesis because of his commitment to the strategy of analyzing experience into its elements. The Gestalt approach, which will be represented in the companion volume to the present one, denies the necessity, or even the appropriateness, of analysis, and starts with unanalyzed phenomena as basic data. This strategy entirely bypasses the problem of synthesis. That "the whole is more than the sum of its parts" poses no special problem for the Gestaltist, as it did for Wundt and the Structuralists. Organization, integrity, and patterning are considered as basic characteristics of perceptual phenomena and need no special explanation.

Thus, Wundt and the Gestaltists agree on the nature of raw, unanalyzed experience. Their disagreement stems from differences in procedure, which in turn reflects an entirely different philosophical approach to nature in general and man in particular.

The final passage in this chapter has already been alluded to. In it, Binet, originator of intelligence testing, describes some observations on the ideational effects of stimulation of which the individual is unaware. Thus Binet, like Mill and Helmholtz, writes of unconscious processes and of their influence on the direction and organization of perception and thought; but Binet's unconscious events are much more like Freud's than are those of his predecessors. Or perhaps it would be historically more accurate to say that Freud's concept of unconscious processes is more like Binet's than it is like that of Mill and Helmholtz. After all, Freud and Binet shared in the same tradition, the dynamic psychiatry of Charcot and Janet.

As with the Gestaltists, Freud is not represented in this volume, even though he was already making contributions to psychological theory in the nineteenth century. His influence on perceptual theory and research however, is, more of an event of the twentieth century than of the nineteenth. For our purposes, Binet can serve as the spokesman for the dynamic view of unconscious processes.

Binet's work, described in the excerpt below, is also of interest in its own right. While it appears to be virtually unknown to contemporary American psychologists it is truly paradigmatic of the recent controversial research on "subliminal perception." For those who despair that there is nothing new under the sun, Binet provides an excellent case in point.

Alfred Binet

Ideas of Subconscious Origin

In the researches which we are at present expounding on the co-operation of separate consciousnesses, we have seen so far that the idea conceived, the will to perform an action, and finally the point of departure and the initiative of the phenomenon belong in the principal consciousness—in that which speaks through the mouth of the waking subject. The *rôles* may be reversed and the whole trend of events take on another phase. The initiative may

A. Binet. Alterations of personality. New York: D. Appleton & Co., 1896, pp. 204–215. Trans. by Helen G. Baldwin from Binet's *Les altérations de la personnalité*. Paris: Alcan, 1892.

pass to the secondary consciousness—to that which does not talk, and which in a great many cases remains so rudimentary that it was long construed as only certain insignificant movements. A sensation perceived by the secondary consciousness may happen to rouse an idea which will be transmitted to the first consciousness without the latter's being aware of the origin.

We have assumed that to find any insensible region whatever in the case of a hysterical subject, and to hide this region from his sight by a screen, is sufficient to make him completely ignore all the phenomena that are induced in these insensible parts of his body. This is, of course, only an ideal. A perfect division of consciousness, only possible schematically, is necessary to prevent the subject's normal ego from perceiving anything at all that is happening in a part of his organism. But we made this supposition, at the same time knowing it to be erroneous, because it is necessary to arrange our facts. We can not describe at the same time both the division of consciousness and also the reciprocal influences of the separate consciousnesses which tend to make the division less complete. So we may now return to our first descriptions, and add some reflections which will make them more accurate.

A fact that is quite exact, at least according to my observations, is that the subject does not perceive the stimulations that are applied to an insensible region; he does not perceive them as they really are, and is unable to localize them on the point stimulated. If the palm of his hand is pricked with a pin he does not connect the sensation of pricking with this place; moreover, if he is able to place it he is no longer anaesthetic there. Sensations induced in anaesthetic regions remain, then, unconscious; but they produce other phenomena which penetrate to the normal consciousness; these are ideas, images, and sometimes false perceptions and hallucinations. From this we see that the subject does not perceive the stimulation; but he may have the idea of this stimulation without knowing why and how this idea comes to him.

An experiment may be cited which will enable us better to understand this curious result than a long description would. We take the insensible hand, place it behind a screen, and prick it nine times with a pin. During this time, or after ceasing to prick it, we ask the subject to think of any number whatever and tell us what it is. He replies that he has chosen the figure 9, that is to say, the one that corresponds to the number of pricks. He did not feel the thrust of the pin, he did not know that he had been pricked, he was anaesthetic; but nevertheless he must have felt something, as the agreement clearly shows. The stimulus, although neither felt nor perceived by the normal ego, produced a certain effect upon this ego, and caused an idea—the idea of the number of pricks.

This result does not seem strange when we understand completely the nature of these alterations of consciousness. For we see that everything is linked together, and that such and such a fact, which seems strange when looked at separately, is in reality necessary and logical. But general information is not obtainable at once, and when I commenced these studies on anaesthesia I knew nothing whatever of the fact just mentioned, believing myself under illusion when I first found it out. Several times I made notes in my memorandum book of observations during which a hysterical patient, whose anaesthesia had been well under control, declared that at a certain time she had guessed what was being done to the anaesthetic region. One day a woman, named Mel., whose right arm was anaesthetic, who had been made to write the world Salpétrière, declared this word had appeared to her "written in white on a black ground," and yet she had not seen her hand, and had not felt either contact or pricks. I wrote down this strange fact, but, being occupied with other researches, did not continue this one. Two years later I had occasion to resume my studies on hysterical anaesthesia. I carried on the examination of this question systematically, and was not long in ascertaining that, as a matter of fact, a stimulus that is not felt may yet cause an idea in the mind of the patient.

Finally, this is the way it seems to me the process should be represented to oneself in order fully to comprehend it. All sensorial stimulation produces in a normal individual the suggestion of a series of associated images. A normal individual has consciousness of all that, as well of the images that are conjured up, as of the sensation that is the point of departure for them. With the hysterical patient the stimulating sensation remains in the dark; it continues unconscious, but it retains its suggestive quality, and

continues to call up the same train of images as if it were perceived and recognised. The process, therefore, develops naturally.
If six pricks are made on the back of a sensible hand, the subject
will count them and consequently will think of the number six
just as a normal individual would, only with the hysterical patient
the first part of the process happens in one consciousness and the
second in another.

We will find more than one example of these psychological
phenomena in observations on suggestion that have been reported
by other authors. I shall designate them for study under the
phrase *suggestions from unconscious indications.* The particular
characteristic of the experiments which I shall now describe is
that the unperceived stimulation rouses associations of natural
and, to a certain extent, normal ideas. The idea of number occurring after a succession of pricks is by no means an artificial idea;
it unites perception and represents it under a different form. It is
very curious to see these natural associations preserved notwithstanding the mental disintegration, and serving as a connecting
link between separate consciousnesses that have no longer any
knowledge of each other.

There is then an idea of subconscious origin which rises in the
normal consciousness of the hysterical patient. What becomes of
this idea? What form will it take? What events will it call forth?
A multitude of complications may arise here, of which I shall
show several examples elsewhere, where other facts borrowed
from mental pathology may be cited in confirmation of these.

Sometimes the subconscious idea becomes a voice that talks to
the subject, and advises or threatens him; sometimes it is the
source of a motor impulse, and induces movements, actions, etc.;
it may also give rise to delirium. Nothing of this kind took place
with my subjects—I do not know why. Experimentation keeps
concealed many artificial conditions which turn the event in one
or another of many possible directions. My experiments took the
direction of the visual sense; the idea suggested by subconscious
sensations has always been a visual idea, and has often amounted
to a hallucination of vision.

I do not believe that my own suggestions contributed considerably in giving this form to the suggested ideas, for it was a long

time before I understood the fact. When I gave three stimulations, for example, to an anaesthetic hand, the subject simply replied to the question "What are you thinking of?" "I am thinking of the number three." This reply indicated nothing more to me than any other idea of an abstract kind might have done. But little by little the replies became more precise. The subject said, "I am thinking of three in the shape of three points"; another, " I see bars and clubs"; or a third, "I see columns." I did not know what to think of these eccentricities, and I set it down to the patient's imagination; but one day it suddenly came to me that the subject saw points when I pricked him, and bars and clubs when I moved his anaesthetic finger. Undoubtedly, it was a visual image of his hand or of the stimulation that appeared to him, and then all my subsequent experiments confirmed this interpretation.

We may now proceed to study two principal points: first, what are the unconscious stimulations that may indirectly affect the normal consciousness of the subject; and, second, under what form do these stimulations penetrate to consciousness.

All stimulations of an anaesthetic sensorial organ may arouse conscious ideas through suggestion. I have already cited tactile stimulations in this connection, and it may now be added that the same result is reached by operating with the muscular sense. If the hand is made to write a letter or word, the subject, asked to think of a letter or word, may indicate those that he has written unconsciously. Likewise, if the same movement is communicated several times to a finger, the number of these movements will decide the number in his mind. By laying raised letters or drawings on the skin the image of the letters and drawings may be produced in the subject's mind—he will speak of them if he is asked what he is thinking about. It will also be seen that through such influences the subject may represent his anaesthetic hand or arm to himself in exactly the position in which it has been placed out of his sight. It is also sufficient to ask him to think of any part of his hand whatever in order to find that it is the part that has been pricked, which proves that he localizes the stimulation somewhat, although he does not perceive it. These processes furnish an indirect means of measuring the sensibility of an anaesthetic member with an aesthesiometer. Things occur in a general way as if the subject got the stimulation translated into the language of another than the tactile or muscular sense. In this way all the details of the tactile stimulation which can be translated, for example, into visual language will be retained.

The experiment might be conducted in such a manner as to make the stimulation no longer of sensorial but of intellectual nature. We may make the anaesthetic hand write several figures and place them under one another as if arranging them for addition; the subject's ego will think, not of the whole series of these figures, but of the total number.

These different kinds of stimulation do not always produce the psychical effects of which we have spoken. If the subject is very much occupied it is quite possible that the slight effect of the stimulations will not be caught or noticed. The patient must be spoken to, made to sit down where there is no noise, with his insensible hand hidden before it is stimulated. It is probable that the unconscious personality which is in all hysterical patients will very quickly understand the experimenter's thought; it hears him question the subject and ask him to think of a number; at the same time it perceives that the experimenter gives a number determined by pricks to the insensible hand. With a little perspicacity he ought to understand the aim of the research; then he enters into it and endeavours to influence the normal consciousness of the subject. He suggests to it in his turn, as he does under many other circumstances, as we shall see further on. . . . I have not the slightest doubt that it is this unconscious personality that *whispers* to the first consciousness the idea of the number, and the latter receives the idea without knowing whence it comes. I do not believe, therefore, that the process can be described as a series of associations of ideas; that requires action and reaction of a more complicated kind.

Let us pass from this rather obscure aspect of the question and reach the final result. The idea, whose origin we have studied, appears in the normal consciousness; let us say, for example, that it is an idea of number; nine pricks have been made on the anaesthetic hand, and the subject thinks of the number nine. How has he come to select this number? One might think that he had counted the sensations, and of course it is evident that some one must have counted them in order to know the sum. But this some one is often not the normal consciousness. The normal consciousness knows nothing of it all. The subject can only say one thing, and that is that he thought of the figure 9. Another consciousness has made the addition and given it to him all ready; he only knows the total.

The subject, ignorant of the origin of nine, does not hesitate to claim it as his own. He is under the illusion that he has chosen this number freely, and he is persuaded that if he had cared to he would have been able to choose some other. But by repeating the same experiment he is shown that the contrary is the case, and that he is placed under the temporary impossibility of thinking of any other figure than that one. I have sometimes made use of the following device, which puzzles a great many patients: Any number whatever, say three, is written on a piece of paper, which is folded up and given to the patient, who is asked to choose any number he likes and to think of it for a few moments. While the patient is determining on the figure his anaesthetic hand is pricked three times, which obliges him to think of the figure 3. Then when he announces this three that he believes he has chosen at random, he is told to unfold the paper and is shown that his thought was foreseen. The success of this little experiment is almost certain.

The foregoing conclusions clearly show that the patient by no means understands the source of the idea that comes suddenly, brusquely, and absorbs the field of normal consciousness. The subjects whom we have studied never—and I desire to emphasize this point—never suspect the origin of these ideas. The division of consciousness has always been complete, absolute, notwithstanding the communications that have been established between the two consciousnesses.

One of the most curious characteristics of this experiment is the state of obsession into which a person is thrown for the moment. This state commences sometimes as soon as the first prick is made. The subject can not think of a number until the series of pricks is ended, even if they were to continue up to a hundred; and, as we have said, it is this number of stimulations that forces itself upon his mind. There are, nevertheless, some subjects who succeed in escaping from this besetting influence by the use of a subterfuge. When asked to think of a number they employ the number of stimulations as if it were a sum of tens, or to insert it in some other combination.

In course of time, when the experiments are repeated, ideas suggested by unconscious perception become extremely intense. I have most often seen them take the form of visual images. The visual image becomes, according to the patients, as dazzling as the sensation of an electric light. It objectifies itself and may obliterate external objects like a real hallucination, to such an extent that a subject who is reading a paper during the experiment is obliged to discontinue his reading, as he no longer sees the printed characters. When subjects reach this degree of sensibility extremely light stimulations immediately appear in visual form, and they sometimes believe that they *see* the stimulus which is brought to bear on the skin.

It will be well to cite an example, in order to give a clear idea of the experiment. One day I applied a steel disk, two and a half centimetres in diameter and having on it a little drawing in relief, to the back of the neck of a young hysterical girl where she was anaesthetic. The disk, which the patient had never seen, of course, was held in contact with the skin for some moments. The patient became restless and complained of dizziness. She saw luminous spots of circular shape that burned before her eyes. Each time that the pressure on the disk was increased the vividness of the sensation increased, and if the pressure became too strong it produced the same effect as a jet of electric light, throwing the patient into catalepsy. But not to go as far as that, let us now concern ourselves simply with the contact, in order to see to what degree the perception of the steel disk is reproduced. In order to avoid questions that might prove suggestive I ask the patient merely to take a pencil and draw what she sees. She is a poor girl without much education, never having been taught to draw, afflicted, moreover, in her girlhood with muscular amyotrophy. All the muscles of the arm which she uses for drawing are atrophied to such a degree that she can scarcely bring it to her head. Notwithstanding these defects she sketched the following drawing, which I figure beside the original, and in order to permit compari-

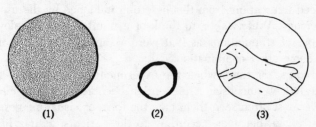

Figure 1. (1) Copy of a design in relief applied to the neck of a subject in order to produce a complex impression of touch; (2) drawing of the impression induced (subject normal); (3) drawing of the impression induced during hysteria.

son, I add a third drawing, made under the same conditions by a normal person. This experiment shows us the very remarkable acuteness of perception of the unconscious subject (Fig. 1).

Three years afterward I again saw the same patient and repeated the same experiment with a different design, and once more obtained a very curious result, which is represented in Fig. 2.

It is possible that these experiments furnish the key of the phenomenon often described under the name of *transposition of the senses,* and which consists in the power of certain persons to see by means of the organs of touch. The details which we have just reported show that the transposition of the senses, while being, strictly speaking, an illusion, nevertheless results from the psychological phenomenon of suggestion of images which is itself real.

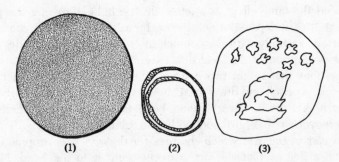

Figure 2. (1) Copy of a design in relief applied on the neck of the subject, as in Fig. 1; (2) and (3) as in Fig. 1.

6

Affect, Consciousness, and Action

The four passages in this chapter are united by a common theme —each insists that muscular response is an integral part of the perceptual process. Brown and Spencer were content merely to emphasize response-feedback as an important source of stimulation, especially that with an affective and aesthetic flavor; their stand is less radical than that of the pragmatic Americans, Dewey and Breese. For Dewey, there is no stimulus without some response to it; similarly for Breese, conscious awareness of any stimulation is contingent on the motor activity it arouses.

The point of view against which these men were arguing—that sensation and action are separate processes—is well entrenched in scientific and in popular thinking. It certainly fits the model fashioned by Bell and Magendie early in the nineteenth century. The existence of separate motor and sensory roots of spinal nerves makes any step to re-unite the two systems, the afferent and the efferent, seem a regressive one. Of course, progress in science is not always unidirectional; it sometimes involves discarding concepts and finding their replacements in the very concepts, though redefined and reworked, that the now discarded concepts had once themselves displaced.

The brief excerpt from Brown and the longer one from Spencer are mainly concerned with the basis of aesthetic feelings. Brown suggests the idea, which is elaborated by Spencer, that optimal utilization of the musculature is accompanied by pleasurable feelings. Those stimuli that afford, or encourage, optimal responding—that is, neither too little nor too much—are perceived as pleasant, and ultimately, at the proper phylogenetic and ontogenetic level, as beautiful.

Provided that she is not too hungry, or otherwise preoccupied with survival, the chicken does cross the road to get to the other side. This simple idea of Brown's that action is intrinsically pleasurable is known to every owner of a pet and every parent of a child. But it is an idea that has had to be discovered anew with each generation of psychologists. Its current champions include, among many others, Nissen, Leuba, Harlow, Hebb, Koch, Berlyne, and White.* The opposition is harder to specify, since it consists more of a tradition than of particular theorists, and since it takes the form of neglecting the idea rather than actively rejecting it.

Thomas Brown

Muscular Sensations

. . . Obscure as our muscular sensations are in common circumstances, there are other circumstances,—which I pointed out to you in treating before of this subject,—in which they make themselves abundantly manifest. I need not refer to the *diseased state* of the muscles, in which they become *painfully* sensible; and I will admit, that the reference to such a morbid state, in which the structure may be supposed to be altered by the disease, would perhaps scarcely be a fair one. It is sufficient to refer to phenomena of which every one must have been conscious innumerable times, and which imply no *disease* nor *lasting* difference of state. What is the feeling of *fatigue*, for example, but a muscular

T. Brown. *Lectures on the philosophy of the human mind.* In four volumes. Edinburgh: W. & C. Tait, 1820. This selection is taken from Lecture XXII in the first volume.

* For specific references and a comprehensive treatment of this literature, see D. W. Fiske and S. R. Maddi (eds.). *Functions of varied experience.* Homewood, Illinois: Dorsey, 1961.

feeling? that is to say, a feeling of which our muscles are as truly the organ, as our eye or ear is the organ of sight or hearing. When a limb has been *long* exercised, without sufficient intervals of rest, the repetition of the contraction of its muscles is accompanied, not with a *slight and obscure sensation*, but with one which amounts, if it be gradually increased, to *severe pain*, and which, before it arrives at this, has passed progressively through *various stages of uneasiness*. Even when there has been no previous fatigue, we cannot make a single powerful effort, at any time, without being sensible of the muscular feeling connected with this effort. Of the pleasure which attends more moderate exercise, every one must have been conscious in himself, even in his years of maturity, when he seldom has recourse to it for the *pleasure alone;* and must remember, still more, the happiness which it afforded him in other years, when happiness was of less costly and laborious production than at present. By that admirable provision, with which nature accommodates the blessings which she gives, to the wants that stand in need of them, she has in that early period,—when the pleasure of *mental freedom,* and the *ambitions* of *busy life,* are necessarily excluded,—made ample amends to the little *slave of affection,* in that disposition to spontaneous pleasure, which renders it almost an *effort* to be *sad,* as if *existence* itself were *delight;* giving him a fund of independent happiness in the very air which she has poured around him, and the *ready limbs* which move through it, almost without his bidding. In that beautiful passage, in which Goldsmith describes the sounds that come, in one mingled murmur, from the village, who does not feel the force of the happiness which is comprized in the single line, that speaks of

"The playful children, *just let loose* from school."

It is not the mere *freedom from the intellectual task* of which we think; it is, much more, that *burst of animal pleasure,* which is felt in every limb, when the long constraint that has repressed it is removed, and the whole frame is given once more to all the freedom of nature. It is by the *pleasure of exertion,* and the *pain of inexertion,* that we are roused from that *indolence,* into which, with great injury to society, that requires our contribution of active aid, we otherwise might sink;—as we are roused, in like man-

ner, by the *pleasure of food*, and the *pain of hunger*, to take the
aliment that is necessary for our individual sustenance; and
though the *mere* aliment is, indeed, more important for *life*, it is
not more important for *happiness* than that pleasure of activity
which calls and forces us from our slothful repose.

> "Thee, too, my Paridel,—I saw thee there,
> Stretch'd on the rack of a too easy chair."

With the same happy provision with which she has considered
the young of our own species, Nature has, in the other animals,
whose sources of general pleasure are still more limited than in
the child, converted their muscular frame into an organ of delight.
It is not in search of richer pasture that the horse gallops over
his field, or the goat leaps from rock to rock; it is for the luxury
of the exercise itself. "If the shell-fish on the shore," say Dr. Fer-
guson, "perform no visible action but that of opening and closing
his shell, to receive the brine that accommodates, or to exclude
the foul matter that annoys him, there are other animals that, in
the opposite extreme, are *active;* and for whom Nature seems to
administer the means of supply, *merely as a restorative of that
strength* which they are so freely to *waste* in the seemingly *sport-
ive or violent exercises to which they are disposed.*"

> "The bounding fawn, that darts across the glade,
> When none pursues, through mere delight of heart,
> And spirits buoyant, with excess of glee;
> The horse as wanton, and almost as fleet,
> That skims the spacious meadow at full speed,
> Then stops, and snorts, and, throwing high his heels,
> Starts to the voluntary race again;
> The very kine, that gambol at high noon,—
> The total herd,—receiving first from one,
> That leads the dance, a summons to be gay;
> Though wild their strange vagaries, and uncouth
> Their efforts, yet resolved, with one consent,
> To give such act and utterance as they may
> To ecstacy, too big to be suppress'd." *

* Cowper's Task, Book IV.

It is this appearance of *happy life* which spreads a charm over every little group, with which Nature animates her scenery; and he who can look without interest on the young lamb, as it frolics around the bush, may gaze, indeed, on the magnificent landscape as it opens before him,—but it will be with an eye which looks languidly, and in vain, for pleasure which it cannot find.

* * *

The idea that action is pleasurable or "rewarding," to use the modern terminology, is frequently seen as incompatible with a point of view, typically referred to as homeostatic, that stresses the biological basis and utility of behavior. This latter point of view, in turn, is usually seen as Darwinian in origin; behavior, like anatomical structure, survives if it has survival value. However, the idea of action-for-its-own-sake can easily be accommodated within an evolutionary framework, as the following excerpt from Spencer shows. Of course, Spencer's conception of evolution is primitive and is more Lamarkian than Darwinian, but that is irrelevant to the present issue.

A key concept in Spencer's thinking, though it does not appear in the following excerpt, is that of *complexity*. It is an intuitively appealing concept, but one that has proven especially recalcitrant to satisfactory abstract and operational definition.* The chief impediment here, if one takes seriously Spencer's emphasis on the response, is that the complexity of a stimulus cannot be measured independently of the responding organism; stimulus complexity is a response-inferred measure. Beauty is in the eye-movements of the beholder.

* See, for example, W. N. Dember, and R. W. Earl. Analysis of exploratory, manipulatory, and curiosity behaviors. *Psychol. Rev.*, 1957, **64**, 91–96.

188   Herbert Spencer

Herbert Spencer

Esthetic Sentiments

. . . When we rise from simple sensations to combinations of
them, of kinds that awaken ideas and feelings of beauty, we may,
I think, discern the same general and special truths. The primitive source of aesthetic pleasure, is that character in the combination which makes it such as to exercise the faculties affected
in the most complete ways, with the fewest drawbacks from
excess of exercise. Joined to this comes, as before, a secondary
source of pleasure—the diffusion of a normal stimulus in large
amount, awaking a glow of agreeable feeling, faint and unde-
finable. And, as before, a third source of pleasure is the partial
revival by this discharge of the various special gratifications
connected in experience with combinations of the kind presented.
Let us pause a moment before each of these. Illustrations of
the primary cause will be furnished us by combinations of movements, combinations of forms, combinations of lights, shades, and
colours, and combinations of tones.

Movements of the body pleasurable to self, and associated
with the consciousness of gracefulness (as in skating), are movements of a kind that bring many muscles into moderate harmonious action and strain none. An awkward motion is one that implies sudden change of direction, angularity, destruction of much
momentum, excess of muscular effort; whereas a motion called
graceful—a motion in curved lines, flowing one into another without break, is a motion in which little momentum is destroyed,
no undue exertion thrown on any muscle, no power lost. And
while in the actor the aesthetic consciousness is mainly consti-

H. Spencer. *Principles of Psychology.* Authorized Edition. New York, D. Appleton &
Co., 1896, Vol. II, pp. 638–640, 646–648. First edition published in 1855. This
passage appeared first in the edition of 1872–73.

tuted by this feeling of moderate but efficient muscular action without check, without strain, without loss, the consciousness of gracefulness in the observer, arises in large measure from sympathy with the feelings implied by such motions. Turning to forms, we observe that the delight in flowing outlines rather than in outlines which are angular, is partly due to that more harmonious unstrained action of the ocular muscles, implied by perception of such outlines: there is no jar from sudden stoppage of motion and change of direction, such as results on carrying the eye along a zig-zag line. Here again, then, we have a feeling accompanying an activity that is full, but contains no element of pain from excess. In the more complex combinations, including many forms presented together, it is relatively difficult to trace out the principle; but I see sundry reasons for suspecting that beautiful arrangements of forms, are those which effectually exercise the largest numbers of the structural elements concerned in perception, while over-taxing the fewest of them. Similarly with the complex visual wholes presented by actual objects, or by pictorial representations of objects, with all their lights and shades and colours. The requirements for harmony, for subordination, and for proportion—the demand for a variety sufficient to prevent monotony, but not a variety which too much distracts the attention, may be regarded as all implied by the principle that many elements of perceptive faculty must be called into play, while none are over-exerted: there must be a great body of the feeling arising from their moderate action, without the deduction of any pain from extreme action. . . .

. . . The results of this rapid survey of a large subject, demanding more time and space than I can give to it, may be briefly summed up thus.

The aesthetic feelings and sentiments are not, as our words and phrases lead us to suppose, feelings and sentiments that essentially differ in origin and nature from the rest. They are nothing else than particular modes of excitement of the faculties, sensational, perceptional, and emotional—faculties which, otherwise excited, produce those other modes of consciousness constituting our ordinary impressions, ideas, and feelings. The same agencies are in action; and the only difference is in the attitude of consciousness towards its resulting states.

Throughout the whole range of sensations, perceptions, and emotions which we do not class as aesthetic, the states of consciousness serve simply as aids and stimuli to guidance and action. They are transitory, or if they persist in consciousness some time, they do not monopolize the attention: that which monopolizes the attention is something ulterior, to the effecting of which they are instrumental. But in the states of mind we class as aesthetic, the opposite attitude is maintained towards the sensations, perceptions, and emotions. These are no longer links in the chain of states which prompt and guide conduct. Instead of being allowed to disappear with merely passing recognitions, they are kept in consciousness and dwelt upon: their natures being such that their continued presence in consciousness is agreeable.

Before this action of the faculties can arise, it is necessary that the needs to be satisfied through the agency of sensational, perceptional, and emotional excitements shall not be urgent. So long as there exist strong cravings arising from bodily wants and unsatisfied lower instincts, consciousness is not allowed to dwell on these states that accompany the actions of the higher faculties: the cravings continually exclude them.

This is another mode of stating the truth with which we set out, that activities of this order begin to show themselves only when there is reached an organization so superior, that the energies have not to be wholly expended in the fulfilment of material requirements from hour to hour. Along with occasional surplus nutrition, and along with that variety of faculty existing in creatures to which surplus nutrition is frequent, there occur the conditions making it possible for the states of consciousness accompanying the actions of the higher faculties, to become states sought for their own sakes, apart from ends: whence arises play.

Gratifications that accompany actions, performed without reference to ends, will mostly be those which accompany actions predominating in the creature's life. And hence this first form of them called play, is shown in the superfluous activity of the *sensori-motor* apparatus and of those destructive instincts which habitually guide its actions. When they are established, the higher orders of co-ordinating powers also come to have their superfluous activities and corresponding pleasures, in games and other exercises somewhat more remote from the destructive activities. But, as we see in the mimetic dances and accompanying chants of savages, which begin to put on a little of the character called aesthetic, there is still a great predominance of these substituted gratifications of feelings adapted to a predatory life. And even on reaching those more-developed aesthetic products and correlative feelings which ancient civilizations yielded, we find a like prevailing trait.

When, however, a long discipline of social life, decreasingly predatory and increasingly peaceful, has allowed the sympathies and resulting altruistic sentiments to develop, these, too, begin to demand spheres of superfluous activity. Fine Art of all kinds takes forms more and more in harmony with these sentiments. Especially in the literature of imagination we may now see how much less appeal there is to the egoistic and ego-altruistic sentiments, and how much more to the altruistic sentiments—a trait likely to go on growing.

A final remark worth making is, that the aesthetic activities in general may be expected to play an increasing part in human life as evolution advances. Greater economization of energy, resulting from superiority of organization, will have in the future effects like those it has had in the past. The order of activities to which the aesthetic belong, having been already initiated by this economization, will hereafter be extended by it: the economization being achieved both directly through the improvement of the human structure itself, and indirectly through the improvement of all appliances, mechanical, social, and other. A growing surplus of energy will bring a growing proportion of the aesthetic activities and gratifications; and while the forms of art will be such as yield pleasurable exercise to the simpler faculties, they will in a greater degree than now appeal to the higher emotions.

* * *

Dewey's article, reprinted in full, is another classic in the history of psychology. It is difficult reading partly because of its style and partly because what it proposes is so far out of line with the traditional physiological concept of the reflex arc and its traditional psychological counterpart, the separation of sensation and action.

Dewey's emphasis on action quite obviously placed him, with James, Carr, and Angell, among the leaders of the newly emerging American school called Functionalism, which towards the end of the nineteenth century was the main competitor of the Structuralist school, founded by Wundt and promulgated in the United States by E. B. Titchener and his followers. One can also see in Dewey's article the seeds of two other schools that were to emerge in the early years of the twentieth century. In his attack on traditional separation of sensation and action, Dewey anticipates one of the main tenets of the Gestalt approach—that the parts of a whole do not have a meaningful existence outside of the context of the whole itself. And by arguing that there is no sensation without response (that "the response constitutes the stimulus"), Dewey partially sets the stage for the much more radical position later taken by Watsonian Behaviorism that there can be no scientifically valid study of sensation at all; only responses can be the object of investigation.

One can be impressed with the role of the response in the perceptual process without subscribing entirely to Dewey's position. For example, one can take an interactionist approach, in which the influence on perception of motor activity is acknowledged, or at least is an hypothesis considered worthy of investigation. Such an approach, less extreme than Dewey's, but certainly far from conservative, might encompass items as disparate as the recent work on the disappearance of stabilized retinal images,* and Werner's examination of the laws of development, as presented in his *Comparative Psychology of Mental Development*. According to Werner's argument, sensory-motor interdependence, one form of *syncretism*, is especially characteristic of primitive organisms—animals, children, members of primitive cultures, schizophrenics, and brain damaged persons—and becomes less evident in mature, healthy, civilized human beings.

* See, for example, R. M. Pritchard. Stabilized images on the retina. *Scientific American*, 1961, **204**, 72–78.

Even the latter, however, are more like Dewey's organism than they are like the organism of the classical physiologist and the traditional psychologist.

John Dewey

The Reflex Arc Concept

That the greater demand for a unifying principle and controlling working hypothesis in psychology should come at just the time when all generalizations and classifications are most questioned and questionable is natural enough. It is the very cumulation of discrete facts creating the demand for unification that also breaks down previous lines of classification. The material is too great in mass and too varied in style to fit into existing pigeon-holes, and the cabinets of science break of their own dead weight. The idea of the reflex arc has upon the whole come nearer to meeting this demand for a general working hypothesis than any other single concept. It being admitted that the sensori-motor apparatus represents both the unit of nerve structure and the type of nerve function, the image of this relationship passed over psychology, and became an organizing principle to hold together the multiplicity of fact.

In criticising this conception it is not intended to make a plea for the principles of explanation and classification which the reflex arc idea has replaced; but, on the contrary, to urge that they are not sufficiently displaced, and that in the idea of the sensori-motor circuit, conceptions of the nature of sensation and of action derived from the nominally displaced psychology are still in control.

The older dualism between sensation and idea is repeated in the current dualism of peripheral and central structures and

J. Dewey. The reflex arc concept in psychology. *Psychol. Rev.*, 1896, **3**, 357–370.

functions; the older dualism of body and soul finds a distinct echo in the current dualism of stimulus and response. Instead of interpreting the character of sensation, idea and action from their place and function in the sensori-motor circuit, we still incline to interpret the latter from our preconceived and pre-formulated ideas of rigid distinctions between sensations, thoughts and acts. The sensory stimulus is one thing, the central activity, standing for the idea, is another thing, and the motor discharge, standing for the act proper, is a third. As a result, the reflex arc is not a comprehensive, or organic unity, but a patch-work of disjoined parts, a mechanical conjunction of unallied processes. What is needed is that the principle underlying the idea of the reflex arc as the fundamental psychical unity shall react into and determine the values of its constitutive factors. More specifically, what is wanted is that sensory stimulus, central connections and motor responses shall be viewed, not as separate and complete entities in themselves, but as divisions of labor, functioning factors, within the single concrete whole, now designated the reflex arc.

What is the reality so designated? What shall we term that which is not sensation-followed-by-idea-followed-by-movement, but which is primary; which is, as it were, the psychical organ-ism of which sensation, idea and movement are the chief organs? Stated on the physiological side, this reality may most conven-iently be termed coordination. This is the essence of the facts held together by and subsumed under the reflex arc concept. Let us take, for our example, the familiar child-candle instance. . . . The ordinary interpretation would say the sensation of light is a stimulus to the grasping as a response, the burn resulting is a stimulus to withdrawing the hand as response and so on. There is, of course, no doubt that is a rough practical way of rep-resenting the process. But when we ask for its psychological ade-quacy, the case is quite different. Upon analysis, we find that we begin not with a sensory stimulus, but with a sensori-motor co-ordination, the optical-ocular, and that in a certain sense it is the movement which is primary, and the sensation which is sec-ondary, the movement of body, head and eye muscles determin-ing the quality of what is experienced. In other words, the real beginning is with the act of seeing; it is looking, and not a sensation of light. The sensory quale gives the value of the act, just as the movement furnishes its mechanism and control, but both sensation and movement lie inside, not outside the act.

Now if this act, the seeing, stimulates another act, the reaching, it is because both of these acts fall within a larger coordination; because seeing and grasping have been so often bound together to reinforce each other, to help each other out, that each may be considered practically a subordinate member of a bigger coordination. More specifically, the ability of the hand to do its work will depend, either directly or indirectly, upon its control, as well as its stimulation, by the act of vision. If the sight did not inhibit as well as excite the reaching, the latter would be purely indeterminate, it would be for anything or nothing, not for the particular object seen. The reaching, in turn, must both stimulate and control the seeing. The eye must be kept upon the candle if the arm is to do its work; let it wander and the arm takes up another task. In other words, we now have an enlarged and transformed coordination; the act is seeing no less than before, but it is now seeing-for-reaching purposes. There is still a sensori-motor circuit, one with more content or value, not a substitution of a motor response for a sensory stimulus.

Now take the affairs at its next stage, that in which the child gets burned. It is hardly necessary to point out again that this is also a sensori-motor coordination and not a mere sensation. It is worth while, however, to note especially the fact that it is simply the completion, or fulfillment, of the previous eye-arm-hand coordination and not an entirely new occurrence. Only because the heat-pain quale enters into the same circuit of experience with the optical-ocular and muscular quales, does the child learn from the experience and get the ability to avoid the experience in the future.

More technically stated, the so-called response is not merely *to* the stimulus; it is *into* it. The burn is the original seeing, the original optical-ocular experience enlarged and transformed in its value. It is no longer mere seeing; it is seeing-of-a-light-that-means-pain-when-contact-occurs. The ordinary reflex arc theory proceeds upon the more or less tacit assumption that the outcome of the response is a totally new experience; that it is, say, the substitution of a burn sensation for a light sensation through the intervention of motion. The fact is that the sole meaning of the intervening movement is to maintain, reinforce or transform (as the case may be) the original quale; that we do not have the replacing of one sort of experience by another, but the development (or as it seems convenient to term it) the mediation of an experience. The seeing, in a word, remains to control the reaching, and is, in turn, interpreted by the burning.

The discussion up to this point may be summarized by saying that the reflex arc idea, as commonly employed, is defective in that it assumes sensory stimulus and motor response as distinct psychical existences, while in reality they are always inside a coordination and have their significance purely from the part played in maintaining or reconstituting the coordination; and (secondly) in assuming that the quale of experience which precedes the "motor" phase and that which succeeds it are two different states, instead of the last being always the first reconstituted, the motor phase coming in only for the sake of such mediation. The result is that the reflex arc idea leaves us with a disjointed psychology, whether viewed from the standpoint of development in the individual or in the race, or from that of the analysis of the mature consciousness. As to the former, in its failure to see that the arc of which it talks is virtually a circuit, a continual reconstitution, it breaks continuity and leaves us nothing but a series of jerks, the origin of each jerk to be sought outside the process of experience itself, in either an external pressure of "environment," or else in an unaccountable spontaneous variation from within the "soul" or the "organism." As to the latter, failing to see the unity of activity, no matter how much it may prate of unity, it still leaves us with sensation or peripheral stimulus; idea, or central process (the equivalent of attention); and motor response, or act, as three disconnected existences, having to be somehow adjusted to each other, whether through the intervention of an extra-experimental soul, or by mechanical push and pull.

Before proceeding to a consideration of the general meaning for psychology of the summary, it may be well to give another descriptive analysis, as the value of the statement depends entirely upon the universality of its range of application. For such an instance we may conveniently take Baldwin's analysis of the reactive consciousness. In this there are, he says . . . "three elements corresponding to the three elements of the nervous arc. First, the receiving consciousness, the stimulus—say a loud, unexpected sound; second, the attention involuntarily drawn, the registering element; and, third, the muscular reaction following upon the sound—say flight from fancied danger." Now, in the first place, such an analysis is incomplete; it ignores the status prior to hearing the sound. Of course, if this status is irrelevant to what happens afterwards, such ignoring is quite legitimate. But is it irrelevant either to the quantity or the quality of the stimulus?

If one is reading a book, if one is hunting, if one is watching in a dark place on a lonely night, if one is performing a chemical experiment, in each case, the noise has a very different psychical value; it is a different experience. In any case, what proceeds the "stimulus" is a whole act, a sensori-motor coordination. What is more to the point, the "stimulus" emerges out of this coordination; it is born from it as its matrix; it represents as it were an escape from it. I might here fall back upon authority, and refer to the widely accepted sensation continuum theory, according to which the sound cannot be absolutely *ex abrupto* from the outside, but is simply a shifting of focus of emphasis, a redistribution of tensions within the former act; and declare that unless the sound activity had been present to some extent in the prior coordination, it would be impossible for it now to come to prominence in consciousness. And such a reference would be only an amplification of what has already been said concerning the way in which the prior activity influences the value of the sound sensation. Or, we might point to cases of hypnotism, monoidealism and absent-mindedness, like that of Archimedes, as evidences that if the previous coordination is such as rigidly to lock the door, the auditory disturbance will knock in vain for admission to consciousness. Or, to speak more truly in the metaphor, the auditory activity must already have one foot over the threshold, if it is ever to gain admittance.

But it will be more satisfactory, probably, to refer to the biological side of the case, and point out that as the ear activity has been evolved on account of the advantage gained by the whole organism, it must stand in the strictest histological and physiological connection with the eye, or hand, or leg, or whatever other organ has been the overt center of action. It is absolutely impossible to think of the eye center as monopolizing consciousness and the ear apparatus as wholly quiescent. What happens is a certain relative prominence and subsidence as between the various organs which maintain the organic equilibrium.

Furthermore, the sound is not a mere stimulus, or mere sensation; it again is an act, that of hearing. The muscular response is involved in this as well as sensory stimulus; that is, there is a certain definite set of the motor apparatus involved in hearing just as there is in subsequent running away. The movement and posture of the ear, the tension of the ear muscles, are required for the "reception" of the sound. It is just as true to say that the sensation of sound arises from a motor response as that the running away is a response to the sound. This may be brought out by reference to the fact that Professor Baldwin, in the passage quoted, has inverted the real order as between his first and second elements. We do not have first a sound and then activity of attention, unless sound is taken as mere nervous shock or physical event, not as conscious value. The conscious sensation of sound depends upon the motor response having already taken place; or, in terms of the previous statement (if stimulus is used as a conscious fact, and not as a mere physical event) it is the motor response or attention which constitutes that, which finally becomes the stimulus to another act. Once more, the final "element," the running away, is not merely motor, but is sensori-motor, having its sensory value and its muscular mechanism. It is also a coordination. And, finally, this sensori-motor coordination is not a new act, supervening upon what preceded. Just as the "response" is necessary to constitute the stimulus, to determine it as sound and as this kind of sound, of wild beast or robber, so the sound experience must persist as a value in the running, to keep it up, to control it. The motor reaction involved in the running is, once more, into, not merely to, the sound. It occurs

to change the sound, to get rid of it. The resulting quale, whatever it may be, has its meaning wholly determined by reference
to the hearing of the sound. It is that experience mediated. What
we have is a circuit, not an arc or broken segment of a circle.
This circuit is more truly termed organic than reflex, because
the motor response determines the stimulus, just as truly as sensory stimulus determines movement. Indeed, the movement is
only for the sake of determining the stimulus, of fixing what
kind of a stimulus it is, of interpreting it.

I hope it will not appear that I am introducing needless re-
finements and distinctions into what, it may be urged, is after
all an undoubted fact, that movement as response follows sensation as stimulus. It is not a question of making the account of
the process more complicated, though it is·always wise to beware
of that false simplicity which is reached by leaving out of account
a large part of the problem. It is a question of finding out what
stimulus or sensation, what movement and response mean; a
question of seeing that they mean distinctions of flexible function
only, not of fixed existence; that one and the same occurrence
plays either or both parts, according to the shift of interest; and
that because of this functional distinction and relationship, the
supposed problem of the adjustment of one to the other, whether
by superior force in the stimulus or an agency *ad hoc* in the center or the soul, is a purely self-created problem.

We may see the disjointed character of the present theory, by
calling to mind that it is impossible to apply the phrase "sensori-
motor" to the occurrence as a simple phrase of description; it
has validity only as a term of interpretation, only, that is, as
defining various functions exercised. In terms of description, the
whole process may be sensory or it may be motor, but it cannot
be sensori-motor. The "stimulus," the excitation of the nerve
ending and of the sensory nerve, the central change, are just as
much, or just as little, motion as the events taking place in the
motor nerve and the muscles. It is one uninterrupted, continuous
redistribution of mass in motion. And there is nothing in the
process, from the standpoint of description, which entitles us to
call this reflex. It is redistribution pure and simple; as much so
as the burning of a log, or the falling of a house or the movement

of the wind. In the physical process, as physical, there is nothing which can be set off as stimulus, nothing which reacts, nothing which is response. There is just a change in the system of tensions.

The same sort of thing is true when we describe the process purely from the psychical side. It is now all sensation, all sensory quale; the motion, as physically described, is just as much sensation as is sound or light or burn. Take the withdrawing of the hand from the candle flame as example. What we have is a certain visual-heat-pain-muscular-quale, transformed into another visual-touch-muscular-quale—the flame now being visible only at a distance, or not at all, the touch sensation being altered, etc. If we symbolize the original visual quale by v, the temperature by h, the accompanying muscular sensation by m, the whole experience may be stated as vhm-vh$m$-vhm'; m being the quale of withdrawing, m' the sense of the status after the withdrawal. The motion is not a certain kind of existence; it is a sort of sensory experience interpreted, just as is candle flame, or burn from candle flame. All are on a par.

But, in spite of all this, it will be urged, there is a distinction between stimulus and response, between sensation and motion. Precisely; but we ought now to be in a condition to ask of what nature is the distinction, instead of taking it for granted as a distinction somehow lying in the existence of the facts themselves. We ought to be able to see that the ordinary conception of the reflex arc theory, instead of being a case of plain science, is a survival of the metaphysical dualism, first formulated by Plato, according to which the sensation is an ambiguous dweller on the border land of soul and body, the idea (or central process) is purely psychical, and the act (or movement) purely physical. Thus the reflex arc formulation is neither physical (or physiological) nor psychological; it is a mixed materialistic-spiritualistic assumption.

If the previous descriptive analysis has made obvious the need of a reconsideration of the reflex arc idea, of the nest of difficulties and assumptions in the apparently simple statement, it is now time to undertake an explanatory analysis. The fact is that stimulus and response are not distinctions of existence, but teleological distinctions, that is, distinctions of function, or part

played, with reference to reaching or maintaining an end. With
respect to this teleological process, two stages should be discrim-
inated, as their confusion is one cause of the confusion attending the whole matter. In one case, the relation represents an
organization of means with reference to a comprehensive end.
It represents an accomplished adaptation. Such is the case in all
well developed instincts, as when we say that the contact of eggs
is a stimulus to the hen to set; or the sight of corn a stimulus
to peck; such also is the case with all thoroughly formed habits,
as when the contact with the floor stimulates walking. In these
instances there is no question of consciousness of stimulus *as*
stimulus, of response *as* response. There is simply a continuously
ordered sequence of acts, all adapted in themselves and in the
order of their sequence, to reach a certain objective end, the reproduction of the species, the preservation of life, locomotion
to a certain place. The end has got thoroughly organized into
the means. In calling one stimulus, another response we mean
nothing more than that such an orderly sequence of acts is taking place. The same sort of statement might be made equally
well with reference to the succession of changes in a plant, so
far as these are considered with reference to their adaptation to,
say, producing seed. It is equally applicable to the series of events
in the circulation of the blood, or the sequence of acts occurring
in a self-binding reaper.

Regarding such cases of organization viewed as already attained, we may say, positively, that it is only the assumed common reference to an inclusive end which marks each member off
as stimulus and response, that apart from such reference we have
only antecedent and consequent; in other words, the distinction
is one of integration. Negatively, it must be pointed out that it
is not legitimate to carry over, without change, exactly the same
order of considerations to cases where it is a question of *conscious*
stimulation and response. We may, in the above case, regard, if
we please, stimulus and response each as an entire act, having
an individuality of its own, subject even here to the qualification
that individuality means not an entirely independent whole, but
a division of labor as regards maintaining or reaching an end.
But in any case, it is an act, a sensori-motor coordination, which

stimulates the response, itself in turn sensori-motor, not a sensation which stimulates a movement. Hence the illegitimacy of
identifying, as is often done, such cases of organized instincts or
habits with the so-called reflex arc, or of transferring, without
modification, considerations valid of this serial coordination of
acts to the sensation-movement case.

The fallacy that arises when this is done is virtually the psychological or historical fallacy. A set of considerations which
hold good only because of a completed process, is read into the
content of the process which conditions this completed result. A
state of things characterizing an outcome is regarded as a true
description of the events which lead up to this outcome; when,
as a matter of fact, if this outcome had already been in existence,
there would have been no necessity for the process. Or, to make
the application to the case in hand, considerations valid of an
attained organization or coordination, the orderly sequence of
minor acts in a comprehensive coordination, are used to describe
a process, viz., the distinction of mere sensation as stimulus and
of mere movement as response, which takes place only because
such an attained organization is no longer at hand, but is in
process of constitution. Neither mere sensation, nor mere movement, can ever be either stimulus or response; only an act can
be that; the *sensation* as stimulus means the lack of and search
for such an objective stimulus, or orderly placing of an act, just
as mere movement as response means the lack of and search for
the right act to complete a given coordination.

A recurrence to our example will make these formulae clearer.
As long as the seeing is an unbroken act, which is as experienced
no more mere sensation than it is mere motion (though the on-
looker or psychological observer can interpret it into sensation
and movement), it is in no sense the sensation which stimulates
the reaching; we have, as already sufficiently indicated, only the
serial steps in a coordination of *acts*. But now take a child who,
upon reaching for bright light (that is, exercising the seeing-
reaching coordination) has sometimes had a delightful exercise,
sometimes found something good to eat and sometimes burned
himself. *Now the response is not only uncertain, but the stimulus
is equally uncertain; one is uncertain only in so far as the other*

is. The real problem may be equally well stated as either to discover the right stimulus, to constitute the stimulus, or to discover,
to constitute, the response. The question of whether to reach or
to abstain from reaching is the question what sort of a bright
light have we here? Is it the one which means playing with
one's hands, eating milk, or burning one's fingers? The stimulus
must be constituted for the response to occur. Now it is at precisely this juncture and because of it that the distinction of sensation as stimulus and motion as response arises.

The sensation or conscious stimulus is not a thing or existence
by itself; it is that phase of a coordination requiring attention
because, by reason of the conflict within the coordination, it is
uncertain how to complete it. It is to doubt as to the next act,
whether to reach or no, which gives the motive to examining
the act. The end to follow is, in this sense, the stimulus. It furnishes the motivation to attend to what has just taken place; to
define it more carefully. From this point of view the discovery
of the stimulus is the "response" to possible movement as "stimulus." We must have an anticipatory sensation, an image, of
the movements that may occur, together with their respective
values, before attention will go to the seeing to break it up as
a sensation of light, and of light of this particular kind. It is the
initiated activities of reaching, which, inhibited by the conflict in
the coordination, turn round, as it were, upon the seeing, and
hold it from passing over into further act until its quality is
determined. Just here the act as objective stimulus becomes transformed into sensation as possible, as conscious, stimulus. Just
here also, motion as conscious response emerges.

In other words, sensation as stimulus does not mean any particular psychical *existence.* It means simply a function, and will
have its value shift according to the special work requiring to
be done. At one moment the various activities of reaching and
withdrawing will be the sensation, because they are that phase
of activity which sets the problem, or creates the demand for,
the next act. At the next moment the previous act of seeing will
furnish the sensation, being, in turn, that phase of activity which
sets the pace upon which depends further action. Generalized,
sensation as stimulus is always that phase of activity requiring

to be defined in order that a coordination may be completed. What the sensation will be in particular at a given time, therefore, will depend entirely upon the way in which an activity is being used. It has no fixed quality of its own. The search for the stimulus is the search for exact conditions of action; that is, the state of things which decides how a beginning coordination should be completed.

Similarly, motion, as response, has only a functional value. It is whatever will serve to complete the disintegrating coordination. Just as the discovery of the sensation marks the establishing of the problem, so the constitution of the response marks the solution of this problem. At one time, fixing attention, holding the eye fixed, upon the seeing and thus bringing out a certain quale of light is the response, because that is the particular act called for just then; at another time, the movement of the arm away from the light is the response. There is nothing in itself which may be labelled response. That one certain set of sensory quales should be marked off by themselves as "motion" and put in antithesis to such sensory quales as those of color, sound and contact, as legitimate claimants to the title of sensation, is wholly inexplicable unless we keep the difference of function in view. It is the eye and ear sensations which fix for us the problem; which report to us the conditions which have to be met if the coordination is to be successfully completed; and just the moment we need to know about our movements to get an adequate report, just that moment, motion miraculously (from the ordinary standpoint) ceases to be motion and becomes "muscular sensation." On the other hand, take the change in values of experience, the transformation of sensory quales. Whether this change will or will not be interpreted as movement, whether or not any consciousness of movement will arise, will depend upon whether this change is satisfactory, whether or not it is regarded as a harmonious development of a coordination, or whether the change is regarded as simply a means in solving a problem, an instrument in reaching a more satisfactory coordination. So long as our experience runs smoothly we are no more conscious of motion as motion than we are of this or that color or sound by itself.

To sum up: the distinction of sensation and movement as stimulus and response respectively is not a distinction which can be regarded as descriptive of anything which holds of psychical events or existences as such. The only events to which the terms stimulus and response can be descriptively applied are to minor acts serving by their respective positions to the maintenance of some organized coordination. The conscious stimulus or sensation, and the conscious response or motion, have a special genesis or motivation, and a special end or function. The reflex arc theory, by neglecting, by abstracting from, this genesis and this function gives us one disjointed part of a process as if it were the whole. It gives us literally an arc, instead of the circuit; and not giving us the circuit of which it is an arc, does not enable us to place, to center, the arc. This arc, again, falls apart into two separate existences having to be either mechanically or externally adjusted to each other.

The circle is a coordination, some of whose members have come into conflict with each other. It is the temporary disintegration and need of reconstitution which occasions, which affords the genesis of, the conscious distinction into sensory stimulus on one side and motor response on the other. The stimulus is that phase of the forming coordination which represents the conditions which have to be met in bringing it to a successful issue; the response is that phase of one and the same forming coordination which gives the key to meeting these conditions, which serves as instrument in effecting the successful coordination. They are therefore strictly correlative and contemporaneous. The stimulus is something to be discovered; and to be made out; if the activity affords its own adequate stimulation, there is no stimulus save in the objective sense already referred to. As soon as it is adequately determined, then and then only is the response also complete. To attain either, means that the coordination has completed itself. Moreover, it is the motor response which assists in discovering and constituting the stimulus. It is the holding of the movement at a certain stage which creates the sensation, which throws it into relief.

It is the coordination which unifies that which the reflex arc concept gives us only in disjointed fragments. It is the circuit within which fall distinctions of stimulus and response as functional phases of its own mediation or completion. The point of this story is in its applications; but the application of it to the question of the nature of psychical evolution, to the distinction between sensational and rational consciousness, and the nature of judgment must be deferred to a more favorable opportunity.

* * *

Binocular rivalry, discussed by Breese in the final excerpt in this volume, was discovered by Wheatstone and is alluded to in Chapter 4. Though rivalry would seem a likely source of information about perception in general, and especially about perceptual selectivity, attention, inhibition, and their underlying physiological mechanisms, very little more is know about it today than was known to Breese over 60 years ago.

The pertinence of rivalry to the present chapter lies in the way Breese uses his research on the phenomenon to draw conclusions about the mechanism of inhibition and the conditions necessary for conscious experience. Breese, whose functionalistic bias was acquired at Columbia under Cattell, rather than from the Chicago Functionalists, nevertheless comes up with a theoretical account of consciousness that is very similar to Dewey's; those stimuli are present in conscious awareness that arouse some motor activity. Conversely, those stimuli which are incapable of eliciting action, or have temporarily lost that capacity (perhaps in competition with stimuli which are prepotent), are inhibited and disappear from consciousness.

Burtis Burr Breese

Binocular Rivalry

If corresponding points of the two retinae are separately stimulated with two incongruous fields—*i. e.*, fields of sufficient difference to prevent their interpretation as a single field—the phenomenon of binocular rivalry appears. For a time one field presses itself into consciousness, then the other takes its place. In this manner a continual shifting of the fields takes place. If a green glass is held before one eye and a red glass before the other, and the eyes turned toward the sky, the struggle of colors is very readily seen. A simple way of getting rivalry between the two eyes is to close both eyes, cover one of them with the hand and turn the face toward the bright sky. The dark and the light fields will be seen alternately.

The stereoscope affords a convenient means of separating the two fields. If a simple drawing of two perpendicular parallel lines is so placed in the stereoscope that it can be seen by the right eye only, and another drawing of two horizontal parallel lines is placed so that it can be seen by the left eye alone, the cross which results shows at the point of intersection a rivalry of the two sets of lines. For an instant they will appear as in *a*, Fig. 1. The next instant they will appear as in *b*, same figure. The fluctuations will continue indefinitely.

Several explanations of this phenomenon have been offered. Helmholtz was the first investigator who studied binocular rivalry carefully. He concluded that the change of fields is due to a change of attention—*i. e.*, the rivalry is psychical, and not physical. If the attention is held upon one of the fields, it will

B. B. Breese. On inhibition. *Psychol. Monogr.*, 1899, 3, #1 (Whole #11). This selection is from pp. 18–21, 44–48, 59–60.

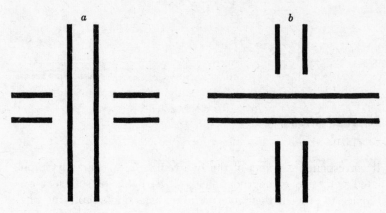

Figure 1

remain in consciousness to the exclusion of the other field. He further states that the rivalry does not depend upon any organic structure or condition of the nervous system, but upon mental conditions. The fact that rivalry does take place is explained by the fact that the attention is ever seeking something new. It does not ordinarily maintain itself in a state of rest, but is constantly changing. If we wish to hold any object in consciousness, we may do so by constantly finding new elements or aspects in it for consciousness. Accordingly, Helmholtz believes that the rivalry between the two retinae can be controlled at will—*i. e.*, if the attention is held upon one of the two fields by force of will power, that field will remain in consciousness.

Hering and Panum consider that binocular rivalry is due *purely* to physiological conditions. Fechner opposes the attention theory of Helmholtz, and Woinow seems to agree completely with Helmholtz.

Chauveau thinks that the phenomenon of binocular rivalry is central, and not peripheral, as Panum suggests. He proposes the hypothesis, as the physiological basis of the rivalry, that the central cells for corresponding points in the retinae are connected with a single optical center, from which visual center the perception of sight arises. When corresponding points of the retinae are stimulated by the same or like objects the corresponding central cells give the same report to the optical center, and hence there is no conflict; but when corresponding points are stimulated by different objects, then the reports which the single optical center receives conflict and perception is interfered with. In favor of this theory is the fact that parts of the field which fall upon adjacent points of the retinae do not show rivalry, but are fixed in consciousness, showing that the retina itself does not possess any noticeable functional rhythm similar to the rhythm of binocular rivalry.

St. Witasek reports that he was able, after practice with the stereoscope, to prevent binocular rivalry of different contours. He used the Zöllner figure, the parallel vertical lines for one eye and oblique lines for the other. He was attempting to get the illusion of the Zöllner figure when its parts were combined by means of the stereoscope. At first the illusion did not appear, because, owing to the rivalry, the lines did not appear simultaneously. After continued attempts he claims that he was able to prevent the rivalry, so that both sets of lines were present at the same time, making the completed figure. This prevention of the rivalry is *very remarkable*. No one has reported such a result before. Neither Helmholtz nor Woinow found that they were able to hold *both* fields in their experiments. They believed that by controlling the attention and fixing it upon one field they could exclude the other; but to hold two different fields in consciousness at the same time, under these conditions, is quite another thing. I have been working two years with the stereoscopic combination of different fields, and have been unable to discover any tendency of the kind mentioned. One of my problems during these two years has been just this attempt to control the rivalry, but I have gained absolutely nothing in my ability to do so; nor have any of my subjects been able to prevent the rivalry. The experiments bearing upon this point will be given later.

The object of my experiments was not so much to find an explanation for binocular rivalry, as to determine what conditions, both subjective and objective, affect it, and to what extent the phenomenon throws light upon the general problem of inhibition.

Apparatus

The stimuli for the retinae were red and green squares one centimeter in size. For the greater part of the experiments these two squares were crossed by five black diagonal lines. The lines upon the red field ran from the upper left-hand corner to the lower right-hand corner, while those upon the green field ran from the upper right-hand corner to the lower left-hand corner, so that when the fields were combined in the stereoscope the lines crossed each other at right angles. These fields were placed upon a black cardboard in proper positions for the stereoscope:

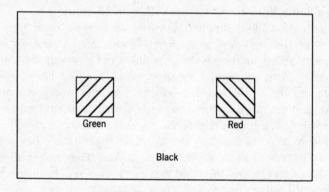

Figure 2

When this cardboard was placed in the stereoscope the squares fell upon corresponding points of the retinae. Red and green backgrounds for the lines were employed merely to aid the subject in determining when the changes in the fields came. If the lines were upon like backgrounds, perception of the exact time the changes occur was more difficult. The colored backgrounds changed in every case with the lines—*i. e.*, the right diagonal lines were always seen upon the red background and the left diagonal lines upon the green. The form of the lines was varied as the conditions of the experiments required. . . .

Summary

The length of time which the fields normally remain in consciousness was increased by direct will power.

Efforts to decrease the number of changes of the fields in a given time were unsuccessful.

With the so-called pure will efforts there were in every case accompanying eye movements.

Elimination of the eye movements decreased the ability to hold either of the fields.

The introduction of conscious eye movements was accompanied by a lengthening of the time of the field whose lines served as the guide for the movement.

Counting the lines upon either field increased the length of time that field remained in consciousness.

Figures which induced the greatest eye movement remained longest in consciousness.

The lines of a moving field remained in consciousness nearly all the time, but did not inhibit the normal rivalry of the two fields.

Contraction of the right side or of the left side of the body had the same effect upon the rivalry, viz., increased the time which the field before the right eye was seen.

Colored borders did not affect the rivalry.

Of two fields of different sizes, the smaller remained longer in consciousness.

Under different conditions adjacent parts of the retinae showed different rates of rivalry at the same time.

Increase in the intensity of the light stimulus caused an increase in the rate of the changes, while the ratio of the phases of the rivalry was normal and constant.

Of two unequally lighted fields, the lighter remained longer in consciousness.

After-images showed the same phenomenon of rivalry; but the changes occurred at a slower rate than in the case of direct stimulation.

When both fields were of the same color the rivalry of the two sets of lines was not affected.

Different stimuli falling upon the same area of the retina of one eye produced the phenomenon of rivalry.

There seem to be some facts in the foregoing experiments that point toward an explanation of binocular rivalry as a purely physiological process. There are others which point to its explanation as a psychical process. The effect which different intensities of light had upon the rate of fluctuation might be interpreted as a purely physiological effect depending upon the anabolic and catabolic processes in the tissue of the retinae. On the other hand, the fact that, of two fields of different intensities, the brighter remained longer in consciousness, seems to point to the attention process as the effective factor. The effect which eye movements had upon the rivalry of the fields may also be looked upon as physiological. These movements brought into activity new parts of the retinae, thereby relieving the parts which had been active in reporting the stimulus to the higher centers. This division of labor enabled the retina to maintain its activity for a longer length of time. Now supposing that these movements, as was the case, were made only when one of the fields was in consciousness, and that when the other field appeared the movements ceased: in the latter case there would be no change of retinal elements; therefore the activity of the retina reporting this field would run down much more quickly. Thus an explanation would be offered for the longer length of time which the other field remained in consciousness. But in all cases of eye movements the fact must be considered that *not one, but both* eyes moved at the same time. Take, for instance, the experiment where eye movements were introduced when the red (right) field was seen. Now, movements along the lines of this field with the right eye were accompanied by movements across the lines of the green or unpresented field by the left eye. So there was a change of retinal elements in this eye as well. When, in the course of the rivalry, the green field appeared and eye movements ceased, then the fixity of the retinal elements was the same for the right eye as for the left. So far as a change of the retinal areas is concerned, the conditions were the same for both eyes. There was a point of difference, however, in regard to fixation. When the red field was in consciousness there was fixation of the lines of that field by the right eye, which was necessary in order to follow the lines. This element of fixation was not possible in the same way for the left eye—*i.e.*, there could have been no adjustment to a particular line as was the case in the right eye. There was, in the one case, a particular and definite motor innervation coming from the cortical centers, while in the other this was lacking. This element was present also to a more marked degree when the lines of one of the fields were counted. Our conclusion, therefore, is that an explanation is to be found, not in terms of the physiological functions of the periphery but in terms of the central processes. This does not mean that it will be in purely psychical terms, for it is evident that the physical movements of the eyes should be considered as an effective factor in the rivalry under the conditions of the experiments.

The introduction of simple figures which tend to induce eye movements strengthened the belief that bodily adjustments play an important part in the phenomenon. But since the effect of these movements is not accounted for in the sense organs of the periphery, it may lie in the relation of the movements to the cortical centers; in other words, in the *meaning value* of the movements for consciousness.

A *purely psychical* explanation cannot stand before the fact that purely mental states were not able to control or affect the rivalry. It continued in its usual rhythm even when the attention was fixed upon one of the fields. In the case of the moving field opposed by a stationary field, the strong attraction which a moving object has for the attention process did not check the rivalry. The other field came and went with about its usual rate. When, however, the so-called pure act of attention was aided by some appropriate motor adaptation, then the effect upon the rivalry was most marked.

In the case of two unequally lighted fields, the brighter calls for a greater number of eye adaptations in the form of more definite and distinct accommodations of the eye to points upon its surface than is the case with the darker field. The darker the field the more even does its surface appear—*i. e.,* the less the degree and the fewer the differences in the surface; it approaches a perfectly plain surface in low intensities of light. Consequently fewer points upon its surface call for fixation. A plain surface is not explored by the eye as thoroughly as a diversified surface is—nothing new is to be gained by such exploration, and so the mind is accustomed to fill in the content at once without the trouble of further eye adaptation. On the other hand, the brighter the field the more points of difference on its surface appear, and consequently the greater the number and more definite the eye adaptations. This was most evident where the red square seen by one eye was opposed to the plain black surface seen by the other eye. Here the black surface was in consciousness but a very small part of the time, the brighter field crowding it out. . . .

In view of these considerations it seems that either a purely physical or a purely psychical explanation of binocular rivalry fails. The true explanation must be looked for in the nature of the psycho-physical processes of the cortical centers, the activity of which depends, not only upon the incoming nerve stimuli, but as well upon the outgoing motor discharges. The character of the discharge which determines into what motor reaction it is to end, is what is meant by the 'meaning value' of bodily movements or adaptations.

Consciousness, from the above point of view, depends for its existence and character upon the transference of sense stimuli into motor paths. This hypothesis considers the incoming, or sense stimulation, and the outgoing, or motor innervation, as a single nerve process. There is no point of separation between them. The motor discharge is necessary in order that any central activity take place. . . .

In emphasizing the importance of the motor elements in emotional states the advocates of the kinaesthetic theory of the emotions consider an emotion as dependent for its character entirely upon the reverberation of the motor adjustments—*i.e.,* upon the complex of sensations coming from movements or adjustments of the body which are the direct reactions of stimuli. That these returning sensations have their particular values for consciousness there can be no doubt, but this is not the relation between consciousness and motor phenomena that I wish to consider. These movements and adjustments from this point of view may be considered in the same way as other external stimuli. The question is, Why and under what conditions do stimuli reach consciousness at all? It is my belief that no stimulus, either external or internal, is presented to consciousness without a motor reaction as a basis of the presentation. In other words, the *condition of consciousness is the transference of the action of the stimulus into or toward motor activity.*

The value of the motor side of consciousness from this point of view is not the value of the sensations coming from acting muscles, but rather the more fundamental fact that incoming stimuli are transformed into outgoing channels. Necessary to this conception is the following hypothesis concerning the action of the brain centers in their relation to afferent and efferent nerve fibers. The condition for the presentation of any stimulus is the permeability of the motor paths from the cortical centers—*i. e.,* consciousness arises only when the cortical centers involved are ready to discharge toward the periphery. The character of the mental state is determined by the location of the discharging centers. Its existence depends upon the *condition* of the motor paths: if they are open, the physiological nervous process necessary for consciousness can take place; but if they are closed, it can not. This conception regards whatever activity or change takes place in the so-called sensory and motor nerves and their centers as a *single* and *unified* process. The analysis of this process into a sensory process and a motor process, and the implied supposition that consciousness may accompany one, or both, is opposed by the above point of view. The sensory and the motor processes are inseparable. Activity in one part of a nerve circuit means activity in every part of that circuit, or, perhaps a better way of expressing it, the cortical centers are active only in transferring stimuli, external or internal, into motor channels. If the stimuli find a blocked system of motor channels from any cortical center, there is no activity of that center, and consequently no consciousness corresponding to such action. . . .

*   *   *

It is interesting to note that those stimuli which were found by Breese to dominate in the rivalry situation appear describable under Spencer's concept of complexity. It would seem fruitful to entertain the hypothesis that the phenomena variously labeled play, exploration, pleasure, beauty, perceptual dominance, and so forth, and variously accounted for by the authors represented in this chapter and by the many who are not, may be subsumed under a single general theory in which the central concept is *action.*

7

Conclusion

A retrospective view of 19th century work in perception, as sampled in the preceding pages, reveals some obvious characteristics and perhaps a few less obvious trends. First, the characteristics.

The 19th century was a period rich in empirical discovery. Many perceptual phenomena that still engage our interest—for example, the geometrical illusions, reversible figures, after-effects of stimulation, binocular rivalry, backward masking, and color mixture—were first reported then.

Second, the 19th century was marked by considerable progress in elucidating the physiological bases of the various perceptual phenomena. A few of the classical examples of such developments were presented in Chapter 2. In addition to Young's work on the mechanism of accommodation, Bell's discovery of the sensory and motor roots of spinal nerves, Helmholtz's model of the mechanism of color vision, and Müller's speculations on the neural mechanisms mediating qualitative sensory discrimination—the 19th century witnessed the accumulation of data and theory pertinent to the structure and functioning of the nervous system. This was the period when the speed of the nerve impulse was being measured, and fairly accurately so, by Helmholtz and others; when the neurone doctrine was being formulated, primarily by Cajal; when knowledge about the organization of the

nervous system, the ultimate mediator of all behavior, was growing at a rapid rate.

Closely related to the above, but not represented in the present
volume, was the development of psychophysical methodology,
its use in empirical investigations, and the consequent elaboration
of the major psychophysical laws.

A third obvious feature of the 19th century was the flourishing
of the analytic-empiricist-associationistic approach. This point of
view characterized the thinking of the British philosopher-psychologists, several of whom are represented in this volume and
the thinking of the German psychophysiologists (as we would
now call them), such as Helmholtz and Wundt. Of course, the
associationistic approach, though clearly dominant, was not without opposition, but that opposition was only beginning to have
impact toward the end of the century, most particularly in the
form of Gestalt theory.

And herein lies a trend. It is almost universal in human en-
deavor that success breeds opposition, and opposition often
brings defeat. This is true in matters of fashion and taste and
just as true in science. Of course, in the case of scientific fashion,
the length of the cycle may be much longer than in the case of
television comedians or hair styles, running perhaps for centuries
rather than months or years.

Indeed, associationism, though staggered by the Gestalt attack,
is still very much in vogue and, perhaps in a more sophisticated
and somewhat disguised form, still dominates psychological
theory. Hebb's *Organization of Behavior,* one of the most influen-
tial theoretical works in recent years, provides an excellent case
in point. The first trend that is apparent in our selections, then,
is the rise of associationism and of its opposition.

The second trend that appears in a retrospective overview of
the material in this volume relates to the institutional aspect of
psychology, rather than to its content. In fact, it pertains to all
of 19th century science, not just to psychology and certainly not
just to perception. The reference here is to the increased professionalization of psychology—a trend that developed toward the
end of the 19th century and continues to the present date.

The early and middle years of the 19th century were the heyday of the scientific amateur. Who first reported reversible figures? Louis Necker, a geologist. How did his report appear? As a letter to the editor of the *Philosophical Magazine*. But why not? After all, there was no institutionalized psychology in 1832; there were no psychological journals to publish in, no psychology departments, no psychologists.

This picture gradually changed toward the end of the century and began changing at an accelerated pace by the beginning of the twentieth century. The story is familiar to readers of the history of psychology. Laboratories devoted explicitly to psychological research were established by William James at Harvard in 1876, by Wundt at Leipzig in 1879, by G. S. Hall at Johns Hopkins in 1883; journals were founded to publish psychological articles, *Mind* by Bain in 1876, the *Philosophische Studien* by Wundt in 1881, the *American Journal of Psychology* by G. S. Hall in 1887, the *Psychological Review* by Baldwin and Cattell in 1894; departments of psychology were set up in universities and men began to earn doctorates in this new field and to organize themselves in professional associations.

The professionalization of psychology came as a response to a real need, which itself arose out of the increasing tendency to treat psychological issues as scientific problems that are subject to empirical investigation, and require special methods, techniques, and apparatus. The fruits of professionalization—journals, meetings, academic courses, and so on—stimulated further growth in the body of psychological data. As data accumulated, new theories were required to encompass them; as theories developed, data were collected to test them. This ever growing, but increasingly refined, mass of information and speculation provided the rich matrix from which developed the fascinating work in perception of the present century.

Name Index

Addams, R., 80, 81–83*, 86
Angell, J. R., 192
Archimedes, 197
Aristotle, 43, 45

Bain, A., 219
Baldwin, J. M., 198, 219
Baxt, N., 161
Beethoven, L. v., 11
Békésy, G. v., 75
Bell, C., 17, 18–32, 33, 70, 155, 183, 217
Berkeley, G., 101, 156
Berlyne, D. E., 184
Binet, A., 162, 173, 174–182
Blainville, H. M. de, 49
Boring, E. G., 101
Bray, C. W., 75
Breese, B. B., 183, 206, 207–215, 216
Brentano, F., 4
Brewster, D., 72, 85, 86, 89
Brown, T., 102–113, 183, 184–187

Cajal, S. R. y., 34, 217
Carr, H., 192
Cattell, J. McK., 206, 219
Charcot, J. M., 174
Chauveau, J. B., 208
Cheselden, W., 64
Cowper, W., 186
Cormack, R. H., 81

Darwin, C., 187
Dember, W. N., 187
Descartes, R., 100, 155
Deutch, J. A., 77
Dewey, J., 33, 183, 191, 192, 193–206
DuTour, E. F., 129

Earl, R. W., 187
Ehrenfels, C. v., 4
Emmons, W. H., 161

Faraday, M., 85, 86
Fechner, G. T., 4, 94, 208
Fiske, D. W., 184
Flavell, J. H., 77
Freud, S., 162, 174

Gall, F. J., 34
Goethe, J. W., 43
Grimaldi, F. M., 96

Hall, G. S., 219
Hamilton, W., 157–160
Harlow, H. F., 184
Hebb, D. O., 184, 218
Helmholtz, H. L. v., 69, 70–75, 94, 100, 157, 162, 163–170, 171, 174, 207–209, 217, 218
Hering, E., 208
Herschell, J. F., 57
Holmes, O. W., 113
Home, E., 7
Hubel, D. N., 80

* Boldface numbers indicate pages on which the author's original material appears.

221